PLANTS THAT HEAL

PLANTS THAT HEAL

Dr Jaroslav Kresánek

Illustrated by Jindřich Krejča
Cover illustration: Moira Grice

Galley Press

English language edition, designed and produced by
Autumn Publishing Limited, Chichester, England.

Published in this edition by Galley Press,
an imprint of W H Smith & Son Limited
Registered No. 237811 England.
Trading as WHS Distributors,
St John's House, East Street, Leicester LE1 6NE.

ISBN 0 86136 881 9

Translation by Heather Trebatická

© 1982 Slovart Publishers, Bratislava.

Typesetting by Avonset, Midsomer Norton, Bath.
Printed in Czechoslovakia.

CONTENTS

WEIGHTS AND MEASURES

For all recipes and preparations in this book we use the metric system, as do pharmacists and chemists. For more general measurements such as plant sizes the approximate equivalents in customary measures are given in parentheses.

PLANTS —
PART OF THE EARTH'S BIOLOGICAL LABORATORY

The interdependence of living organisms

Plants play an essential role in the functioning of living organisms: only they are capable of preparing from the inorganic substances of nature the complicated organic compounds without which they, and also the Animal Kingdom, could not exist. Plants provide animals with shelter in unfavourable weather and when in danger from other animals. Plants enable animals to make shelters for themselves and build nests. On the other hand, animals have a considerable influence, as decomposers, on the composition of the soil by breaking down dead plant material into its elements. Small flying insects and birds pollinate the flowers of plants and migrating animals carry seeds and fruits great distances.

Plants not only provide Man with food — grain, fruit, vegetables and so on, but also with the raw materials essential for building and carpentry, and for many industries including those based on rubber, textiles, and paper. Wood, coal, peat, and petroleum are of ever-increasing importance, and are all of plant origin. It is no wonder that more and more attention is being devoted nowadays to plants. Mankind is endeavouring to preserve the biological equilibrium of every region and make rational use of water supplies and natural resources. Every region can thus become a permanently fertile, healthy, beautiful environment.

A short illustrated glossary of plant structure

It is not the object of this book to present a complete morphology of plants, for which see a botanical dictionary. Here we present only a selection of medicinal plants — most of them flowering plants — and true-to-life colour illustrations of them. Such plants are composed of three main organs: the root, the stem and the leaf.

The root usually fixes the plants in the soil and grows downwards. It is thin, filiform (1), sometimes conical (2) or napiform (3), and grasses have fibrous roots (4).

The stem (stalk or trunk) supports the leaves and conveys water and minerals from the soil. It is usually cylindrical (6a), sometimes hollow (b), grooved (c), ancipital (7) angular (8), or quadrilateral (a, b). A leafless stem is called a scape (such as the stem of the Cowslip). A metamorphosed stem serving to accumulate reserve substances is a rhizome (5).

The leaf (9) usually has a flat blade (a) with ribs or veins (b), often a petiole (c) and sheath (d). The shape of the leaf (10) is cordate (a), oval (b), lanceolate (c), etc. Simple or segmented (11), its edge is serrate (a), dentate (b), crenate (c), etc; dissected (12), it is lobate (a), where the lobes extend into 1/8th of the width of the leaf, pinnatilobate (cleft) (b), where the lobes reach 1/4 of the width of the leaf, or pinnatifid (c) where the sinuses almost reach the midrib of each leaf. It can also be made up of several leaflets. The petiole which supports the leaf often has a stipule (13).

The flower is a transformation of the original leaf (14); its function is reproduction. The complete flower consists of the floral envelope (made up of an external green calyx (d) with sepals and an internal corolla (c) of petals which are usually coloured; if the floral envelope is not distinct it is called a perianth), a set of stamens (b) forming the male reproductive organs, a pistil (a) and a penduncle (e). The pistil, made up of the ovary, style and stigma, is the female reproductory organ. Other terms are illustrated separately as required.

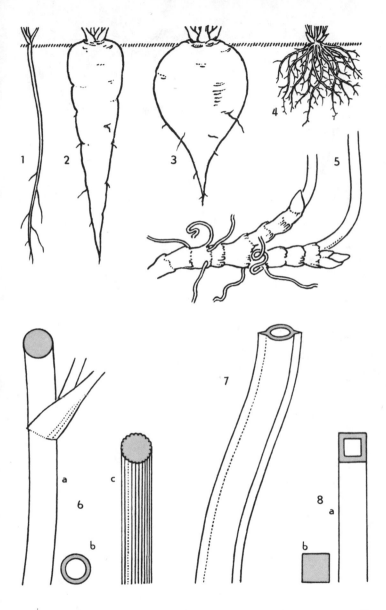

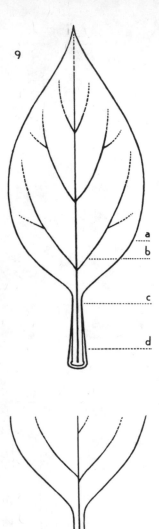

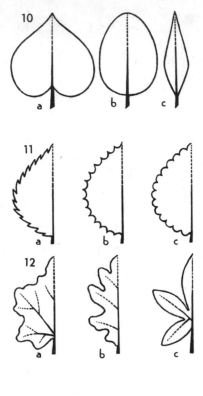

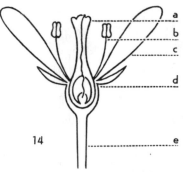

MEDICINAL PLANTS

The medicinal properties of plants

Man has long used plants as medicaments, and has cultivated some of them for thousands of years (flax from 4000 BC, for example). The poisonous properties of many species were well known; an extract of Hemlock was used for executions in Greece and Persia from the 400s BC. In 399 BC the philosopher Socrates was put to death in this way.

The plants we call *medicinal* differ from other plants in that when administered to a living animal (or human being) they have a beneficial effect on the state of health. Medicinal plants rank among the substances we call *medicaments.* From medicaments (healing substances) *medicinal preparations* are produced in the form of solutions, tablets, ointments and so on, which are used as prescribed by a doctor in accordance with the accompanying instructions.

Medicaments are either of *natural* origin — vegetable or animal — or are made *synthetically,* that is by chemical processes. On the whole the trend has been from medicaments (the source being a natural substance processed by chemical means) to substances prepared synthetically, that is by chemistry alone.

In the present period of the scientific and technological explosion — with all its advantages and disadvantages — people are beginning to turn back to natural substances. Natural medicaments are found for the most part in the taller, flowering plants, but they can also be micro-organisms — those producing antibiotics, for example; more rarely they are of animal origin (honey, for example) or mineral origin (e.g. healing mud).

Vegetable medicaments are the product of the metamorphoses of matter — the metabolism of plants, in which they are stored as reserves (e.g. starch) or are secreted by them (e.g. resin). Of the vast number of substances contained by plants only a few can be regarded as medicaments. What is more, the therapeutically effective constituent is usually to be found only in a particular organ, and it is this that is therefore collected. It rarely happens that the whole plant is medicinal. It is usually only the one, sometimes more, of the following: the herbage *(herba)*, the leaf *folium)*, the root *(radix)*, the subterranean stem *(rhizoma),* the flower or part of it *(flos)*, the bark *(cortex)*, bulb *(bulbus)*, wood *(lignum)*, fruit *(fructus)*, seed *(semen)* or pericarp *(pericarpium)*. After processing and conservation the collected vegetable matter is known as a *drug*.

Collecting medicinal plants

The healing properties of plants — their composition, amount and medicinal efficacy — depend on a number of factors, of which the most important are the conditions in which the plant grows, the time of harvesting the relevant part, the method of preservation until the time it is used for medical treatment, and the way it is stored up to that time. These principles are generally valid at any time and therefore certain criteria may be set.

Collection is always made at the time when the plant in question, or its part, contains the maximum amount of active principles, which can be approximated with the vegetational period of the plant.

The time for collection cannot be fixed exactly according to the calendar, however; a hard winter, late spring or cool summer can have a considerable influence on the formation of the active principles.

Aerial parts (those above ground) are collected during fine, sunny, dry weather, but not in excessive heat. Firm containers should be used, preferably baskets.

Leaves are only collected when young, full grown, healthy and clean. This must be done just before the plant flowers, as it is then producing the greatest amount of active principles.

Herbage (leaves, stalks and flowers together) is collected when the plant begins to flower. Healthy stalks, not over-thick, are cut off together with the flowers. In plants with tall stems tending to be woody at the base, the top 15-30cm (6-12in) should be cut off.

Flowers are collected at the beginning of the flowering period. This is because the flower continues to develop after it has been severed from the plant. Sections of the plant, such as the petals, are also included under this heading. The flower is one of the most delicate materials — it must not be crushed or collected in unsuitable containers (polythene bags, for example) or it will 'sweat' and deteriorate in value.

The fruit is collected when it is beginning to ripen — it, too, continues to ripen afterwards. The seeds are removed from the mature fruit.

Bark is collected in the spring when the flow of sap is at its maximum. Firstly two transverse incisions are made 10-20cm (4-8in) apart. These are then joined by a vertical incision, and the bark is detached with a blunt, stainless steel instrument.

Wood is collected from slender trunks or fairly thick branches at the beginning or end of the vegetational period.

It is essential to have the permission of the owner of the tree, and collect bark and wood only from trees set aside for the purpose.

The subterranean parts — the *roots* and *rhizomes* — are usually dug up at the end of the vegetational period, in autumn, when the plant is preparing for its winter 'sleep', or in spring before it begins to 'awaken'. Take care not to damage the roots, and shake off the soil. According to the nature of their active constituents, they can sometimes be washed quickly under running water.

Bulbs and *tubers* are usually dug up in autumn when the aerial parts begin to die off.

The material collected must be clean. It must not include other parts of the plant, to say nothing of other plants or sand, soil and gravel.

Each type of material is collected separately, and it is best to concentrate on only one or two species at a time.

Warning: some plants contain highly active substances harmful and even dangerous to the health, which are *poisonous*. These can be collected only by those specially trained or forewarned of the dangers, never by children. Pickers must not have any open wounds on their hands, and they must not eat, drink or smoke while harvesting. Poisonous plants are never collected at the same time as non-poisonous ones. They are dried and stored separately, or sometimes even sent off to drying sheds. These plants are *never* collected for your own use.

Conservation: Drying

The simplest and most common method of conservation is *drying*. The drying methods used depend on the nature of the active constituents. Drying consists of removing the water content; the change from the fresh state to the dry is not a single process, but it involves a series of processes, the nature of which is not entirely clear. For the most part they involve decomposition and are detrimental to the active constituents. The loss of semipermeability of the cell membranes in a plant's various tissues allows the active substances to react with each other, while in the fresh plant they are kept separate. The process of decomposition varies according to the organ, the type of plant and the time of collection. Decomposition is accelerated by inexpert collection, injuring or crushing the plant and its parts, and by the use of unsuitable instruments and containers. The changes that take place during drying are also influenced by the oxygen content in the air, light, humidity, and above all, the temperature applied. For this reason different temperatures must be used for different plants in accordance with their active constituents. Where no specific instructions are available, preference is given to rapid drying. Most of the active substances are influenced during drying by the enzymes present, which are inactivated at 60°C (140°F). For this reason it seems right to set a high temperature for a short time (3-6 minutes) at the beginning of the drying process. If correctly dried the colour and form of the material dried should remain unchanged (there are some exceptions to this rule, e.g. the pink flowers of the Mallow always turn blue when dried).

Herbs are mostly dried at a natural temperature. A drying place — such as a loft or shed — should be prepared before collection is started. Never collect more than you can dry.

Roughly the drying areas required are as follows: one square metre is sufficient for ¼ to ½kg of fresh flowers — ½ to 1kg of fresh leaves and 1 to 2kg of fresh bark or roots. The aerial parts can also be tied in small bunches and hung up to dry.

Before drying the material collected is examined and sorted; it is not left unnecessarily long in the containers used for collection. It is spread out in thin layers in a clean place, on dry, clean, odourless paper, or even better on rust-free meshed frames which can be placed in stands one above the other and do not require much space. The usual dimensions of the frames are 80-100cm × 100-200cm (30-40in × 40-48in). A suitable thickness for the frame boards is 1.2-2cm × 2-4cm (½-¾in × ¾-1½in). They can also be used for the drying of mushrooms. The material collected must be turned several times during the drying process, and great care should be taken to avoid unnecessary damage. The drying process is completed when the leaves rustle when touched, the stalks and roots break easily, and the flowers crumble to powder. Before storing, the material — now referred to as a drug — is arranged in little heaps and left to 'breathe' — only then is it put in containers (cardboard or metal boxes with airtight lids).

Approximate drying times

Flowers:	in summer 3-8 days	in spring and autumn 8-14 days
Leaves and herbage:	3-14 days	10-21 days
Roots:	14 days	21 days

Storing, sorting, packing and transport of drugs

The storage of drugs is an important factor because it influences their quality and therapeutic value. Humidity, daylight and variations in temperature have a generally harmful effect. The place intended for storage must be well ventilated, dry, and free of dust and foreign odours. In some cases even these conditions are insufficient. Flowers in particular easily become damp, and it is therefore best to store them in previously heated tins, the lids of which are then sealed with adhesive tape; the tins should be reheated and the lids resealed every time they are opened.

For your personal use do not store more of the drug than you need for one year, until the next collection. Then throw away the old material and collect a fresh supply. Never mix them. Stored drugs should be frequently checked — they easily become damp and are often attacked by parasites (Elderberry flowers, Angelica and Dandelion roots, for example, are particularly difficult to store).

If the drugs are to be transported, pack them in clean sacks, each species separately, and with a maximum of 6-8kg (8-18lb) in each sack. The sacks must be carefully sewn up and a list of contents attached.

The cultivation of medicinal plants

Medicinal plants have been cultivated since ancient times. The medieval monasteries had their own gardens, and monks and nuns grew those they needed for their own use. Many medicinal plants are of attractive appearance and make a pleasing addition to the garden. Almost all are nectar-bearing, which is a great advantage if you keep bees. This book does not deal with the cultivation of medicinal plants for commercial purposes, but gives just basic guidelines for cultivation on a small scale.

The cultivation of medicinal plants differs considerably from that of other plants. The aim with most plants is to produce the highest possible yields, whereas medicinal plants are grown for their active constituents, and the aim is to increase these in a certain organ, and sometimes to influence the ratios of the individual elements of the therapeutically active substances. But this can be undertaken only by an expert with considerable know-how.

When selecting medicinal plants for cultivation it must not be forgotten that plants are part of the surrounding environment, where they develop, grow, reproduce and finally die. Two kinds of factors influence the plant's environment: physical and biotic. The most important physical factors are first of all the climate: heat, light, air, precipitation (the plot should not be far from water, so that the crop can be watered); next the edaphic factor: the type and quality of the soil (medicinal plants require good soil); the topographical situation: the position of the site, its relief, and surroundings. The biotic factors include the direct influence of animals, other plants and, above all, Man.

Most drug plants require well-nourished soil. Some of them like a sunny position (Chamomile), some a shady one (Lily-of-the-Valley). Those that need warmth include Wormwood, whereas cool positions are required for Bilberries; the Bogbean demands a damp site; Coriander requires plentiful lime in the soil, whereas Ling hates lime.

The fertilization of medicinal plants is a complex question, requiring a perfect knowledge of the technique of sowing and the composition of the active substances. It is therefore wisest to consult a specialist.

The material for sowing should be obtained from experien(
or from reliable specialized shops. Most drug plants are cu(
other plants: those from which we collect the seeds are
cereals, those grown for their leaves or herbage like fod(
cultivated for their roots or tubers, like potatoes.

Not all medicinal plants are grown from seeds. Some are re(
vegetatively by the different parts of the mother-plant which
and continue to grow: the offshoots, cuttings (parts of the ro(
rhizome which burgeons), the terminal parts of the stem cover
soil or, most simply and most commonly, a clump of roots.

Vegetables and spices

Medicinal plants include some plants which commonly form a part of
everyday food. Apart from various fruits containing valuable vitamins,
there are also certain spices and vegetables. Their immediate effect is
not very marked, however, because the quantities included in food are
minute compared with the doses given medicinally.

Raw, grated Carrot is not only a source of vitamins, but it is effective in
gastrointestinal disorders (especially in babies, but also in adults),
intestinal catarrh and parasitic worms. To take another example: Parsley.
It has a diuretic action and the aerial parts are a source of vitamins
(vitamin C in particular). One of the best-known sources of vitamin C is
Green Pepper, which also improves the appetite. Garlic is very effective
in cases of flatulence, constipation, infectious intestinal catarrh and a
number of other disorders, such as high blood pressure, arteriosclerosis
and insomnia. It is also a good preventive medicine against influenza. It
has one drawback: its pervading smell. In spite of this it is consumed in
considerable quantities, especially in unhygienic environments where it
is often the only protection against infection. Even the builders of the
Egyptian pyramids were aware of this fact — the slaves working on
these constructions were obliged to eat garlic.

Caraway seeds prevent flatulence, which is why they are added, as a
precaution, to bread, green cabbage, and so on.

Of the medicinal plants included in the pictorial section many can be and are used as seasoning. Fennel and Aniseed also serve as a disinfectant, alleviate flatulence and bronchial catarrh, act as an expectorant, etc. Fennel is also believed to increase the secretion of the milk glands in nursing mothers. Horse-radish and Onions have excellent disinfectant properties.

Well-known and popular spices, many of which are grown in rural gardens, include Juniper berries, Thyme, Sage, and so on.

A word in conclusion: when plants are used as spices or flavouring, keep in mind the saying: 'Everything in moderation'.

THE ORIGINS OF NATURAL MEDICINES

The active constituents of drug plants

Plants synthesize elements from the soil and atmosphere which they absorb through their roots and leaves: water, carbon dioxide, and mineral and inorganic matter. The basic process is the photosynthetic assimilation of carbon dioxide, known simply as photosynthesis. The name comes from the Greek *phos*, light, because for the transformation of carbon dioxide and water into organic substances (sugars, oils, proteins) the plant makes use of the sun's energy in the form of light. The first products of photosynthesis are saccharides (sugars), from which simple organic acids arise, fatty acids and amino-acids. These simple substances, which every plant contains, are known as primary metabolites. From these specialized secondary metabolites are created. Together they make up the plant's natural substances, many of which have therapeutic properties.

Of the primary metabolites, the *saccharides* (hydrocarbons) are of medical importance; *starches* (polysaccharides) are frequently used in powders and for the preparation of tablets, etc. *Mucus* is also based on saccharides — it is used as a protective substance — mucilage, alleviating coughs, and so on. Certain *amino-acids* are not produced by the human body but are essential to it, and must therefore be introduced in the form of food. Amino-acids containing iodine regulate the action of the thyroid gland; the more complex ones, such as insulin, are the basic elements in hormones and antibiotics. The most important, however, are the proteins — the primary elements in the living body.

From among the specialized metabolites, the generally yellow-coloured *flavones* are of particular importance: *rutin* strengthens the walls of the capilliaries; others cure various allergies and high blood pressure, assist in the treatment of infectious diseases, and have recently formed the basis of some contraceptive drugs. They generally promote the main therapeutic effects of the active principles in natural drugs. *Terpenes*, found in menthol, camphor, etc., are of special significance. The more complex terpenes (tetracyclic triterpenes) form the basis of steroids, which are found in numerous vitamins (ergocalciferol D$_2$); the *bitter principles* make possible the digestion of fats, the *saprons* are used as expectorants and diuretics, the *digitalins* are the heart medicines found in the foxglove. A very widespread group of secondary, specialized metabolites is formed by the *tannins*, effective in the treatment of diarrhoea, inflammation and so on. A group of *alkaloids* containing deadly poisons are used for a number of medical purposes.

Plant medicine

Phytotherapy, that is medical treatment using plants, dates back to ancient times and has always been preserved in the form of 'popular medicine'. Fresh knowledge about the functioning of the human body and new discoveries concerning the substances contained in the plants and their therapeutic value, have led to a reassessment and revival of the ancient traditions of plant medicine. There are about 380,000 different species of plants in the world, of which only five per cent have been more or less investigated by research workers. This means that there are still almost inexhaustible reserves in the field of phytotherapy.

It would, however, be dangerously fanatical to regard this branch of medicine as the only possible one. Medicinal plants incontestably hold a special position in medicine and are of exceptional importance, but the use of plant drugs without obtaining a correct diagnosis, and often even without consulting a doctor, can be detrimental to the health. NEVER TRY TO TREAT illnesses accompanied by high temperatures, spasms, or acute pain. It is also unwise (with a few exceptions) to drink the same herbal tea over a long period of time; a temporary improvement at the beginning can lead to a later aggravation of the illness.

Preparation of plant medicaments

For internal use, phytotherapy consists of the imbibing of therapeutic drugs, infusions being the simplest form, or the juice of vegetable substances. Externally, tinctures are used for such things as compresses, baths, wet packs, and mouth washes.

Herbal tea mixtures are sold already prepared, but they can be prepared from plants you collect and dry yourself. The rule to follow is: only use the plants which you are quite sure you know, or which you have bought from a specialist. Never mix old drugs with fresh ones, and do not collect plants which are contaminated by dirt or mildew (they may be affected by spores of *Fusarium* fungi, only visible under a microscope, which secrete poisons unaffected by boiling and which decrease the production of red blood cells).

When preparing a herbal tea mixture at home firstly choose the basic drug which determines its therapeutic use *(remedium cardinale)*: then add the auxilliary drugs which increase its effect *(remedium adjuvans)* and finally the drugs which improve its appearance, taste, aroma *(remedium korrigans)*, as indicated for each plant in the special section. A herbal tea should not contain too many different drugs because they can interfere mutually with each other.

Herbal teas are usually drunk warm, even hot (for sweating in cases of colds, etc.) and generally sweetened with honey or sugar — with the exception of cases of intestinal diseases.

There are three main modes of preparation:

1. Maceration or extraction by steeping in water at room temperature (15° to 20°C; 59°-68°F) from 30 minutes to 6-8 hours. Used mainly for extracting mucilages.

2. Infusion or extraction using boiling water: boiling water is poured over the drug and then it is left to stand from 15 to 45 minutes. A more exact method: after infusing the drug, place the container in a water-bath for 5 minutes and then leave to stand 45 minutes, stirring occasionally, then filter. This method of preparation is suitable for drugs containing silica, for example.

3. Decoction or extraction by boiling: boiling water is poured over the drug and left to boil gently for the prescribed time (more exactly: 30 minutes in a water-bath). This method is used for drugs containing tannins, for example.

The methods described above can be combined: a macerated decoction can be prepared, for example. The drug is put to macerate in half the prescribed quantity of water, the extract is poured off and the drug is boiled with the remaining half of the water; the two extracts are then mixed. The maceration of infusions is done in a similar way. The mode of preparation of the extract is determined by the active principles you wish to obtain and by the plant parts involved (the flowers and leaves are usually infused, the hard parts — the bark and roots — boiled).

Before preparing the tea, put the drugs in a sieve and hold it for 5-10 seconds under a weak current of cold water (this frees the drug of dust and swells it slightly). The drugs in the herbal mixture must be prepared carefully, cut up in small particles, usually such as to pass through meshes with openings 3×3mm (¹/₁₀in); finer particles are sieved off, and fruits and seeds are usually crushed. The various drugs must of course be mixed thoroughly.

Tinctures are prepared by maceration of the drug (or fresh plant) in alcohol (usually 85 per cent) at room temperature for a period of 8-10 days in a closed container protected from the light (the drug filling about ⅓ of the container). Medicinal wines are prepared in a similar manner.

Syrups are extracted from drugs (or fresh plants) thickened with sugar.

Alongside the drinking of herbal teas, a recent trend has been the consumption of fresh plants, in the form of spring salads, herbal juices in spring, and juices from medicinal plants throughout the year as therapy during illness.

Spring salads are prepared from the fresh young leaves of practically all edible plants; they are usually not salted, but lemon juice is added. To take an example: the young leaves of Chicory, Dandelion and Ground Ivy are mixed in equal quantities and a little chopped Onion, Parsley and Angelica root added for flavour. The young leaves of Nettles, Daisies, and Summer Savory are also suitable for salads. The principle to remember is: a juicy herb without a marked taste of its own is mixed with a small quantity of a sharp or aromatic one.

A similar principle is also observed in the preparation of the juice of plants for spring cures: basic herbs and added ingredients are mixed in a ratio of 9:1. According to one herbalist, E. Fischer, the basic herb can be Lady's Mantle, Dead-Nettle, St. John's Wort, Yarrow, Marjoram, Silverweed, Shepherd's Purse, Dandelion, Plantain or Veronica; the spicy ingredients Angelica, Elderberry leaf, Saxifrage, Chicory, Ribbed Melilot, Large-flowered Sticky Eyebright, Ground Ivy, Bogbean or Centaury.

To prepare the herbal juice, wash the plants thoroughly, then let the water drip off before putting them through a mincer or crushing them in a mortar. Squeeze the juice through a fine-meshed cloth and put it in a glass container that can be hermetically sealed. The juice is taken by the teaspoonful. It must be prepared the day it is used and kept in a cool place. Recently juices of the plant parts indicated in the pictorial section have been used (they are also produced commercially). The only objection to these extracts is that when prepared at home their composition is not constant, and dosages are therefore only approximate.

An example of a well-known herbal tea mixture for a spring cure is: the leaves of Sage and Rosemary and the herbage of Wormwood (10g of each), the herbage of Yarrow and St. John's Wort (20g of each), Nettle leaves (30g). Pour ¼ litre of hot water over a tablespoonful of the herbal tea and leave to stand for 15 minutes. Three cups a day, before meals.

Recipes for herbal mixtures according to the treatment required

ANTIDIABETIC MIXTURES

Basic drugs: pericarp of ripe Beans — herbage of Goat's Rue — Bilberry leaf.

Examples of herbal mixtures:
> (1 part=a certain weighed amount, e.g. 10g)

25 parts	Goat's Rue herbage
25 parts	Bean pericarp
20 parts	Bilberry leaf
20 parts	Nettle leaf
5 parts	Sage leaf
5 parts	Dandelion leaf

A decoction of 2-3 teaspoonfuls of the drug mixture to 2-3 cups of boiling water; cover and boil 2 minutes, leave to stand 10 minutes, strain into a thermos flask. Drink 2-3 cups 2-3 times a day between meals.

10 parts	Bean pericarp
10 parts	Nettle leaf
10 parts	Birch leaf
60 parts	Bilberry leaf

One tablespoonful of the mixture for one cup of decoction. Drink hot before meals 2-3 times a day.

40 parts	Bilberry leaf
60 parts	Bean pericarp

Two tablespoonfuls are boiled in ½ litre of water. Strain and drink one cup three times a day before meals.

ANTIDIARRHOEIC MIXTURES

Basic drugs: Bilberry leaf and fruit — herbage of Silverweed and all drugs containing tannins.

Examples of herbal mixtures:
20 parts	Silverweed herbage
10 parts	Common Knotgrass herbage
15 parts	Plantain

One tablespoonful of the mixture for one cup of the infusion.

30 parts	Silverweed herbage
30 parts	Peppermint herbage or leaf
30 parts	Balm

One tablespoonful of the mixture for one cup of the infusion.

23

50 parts   Silverweed herbage

One tablespoonful of the herbage to one cup of cold water. Boil ½ minute. Before removing from the heat add a pinch of Peppermint leaf. Drink 2-3 cups a day.

100 parts Bilberries

A heaped tablespoonful to a cup of water. Macerate cold 8 hours. Drink in small doses several times during the day.

10 parts	Comfrey root	15 parts	Common knotgrass
20 parts	Oak bark		herbage
15 parts	Chamomile	15 parts	Plantain
	inflorescence	15 parts	Bilberries

Decoction of one tablespoonful to a cup of water. Drink 2-3 times a day.

ANTIHAEMORRHOIDAL MIXTURES

Basic drugs: a combination of siliceous or mucilaginous anti-haemorrhagics (based on antiphlogistic tannins) — Chamomile (for warm rectal baths) — Oak bark (for lukewarm rectal baths) — herbage of Common Toadflax (20g to ½l milk — mixed to a paste which is applied as a compress to the painful spot.

Examples of herbal mixtures:

30g	Horse chestnut flower	30g	Chamomile inflorescence
20g	Sage leaf		

Boil the mixture in a litre of water and use as a bath (for washing or as a compress).

50g	Oak bark	20g	Horse-tail herbage
20g	Valerian root		(Equisetum arvense)

Boil in one litre of water; leave to cool 10 minutes. For washing and compresses.

ANTIRHEUMATIC MIXTURES

Basic drugs: Birch leaf — Willow bark — diuretic drugs and other drugs increasing the metabolic processes of the organism in general.

Examples of herbal teas:

Equal parts of Sweet Flag and Couch Grass (Quitch) rhizome, Angelica root, Birch leaf and herbage of Motherwort. Three cups a day of the warm infusion made from a tablespoonful of the mixture.

Equal parts of Balm leaf, the herbage of Horse-tail, Hemp Nettle and Common Knotgrass and Dandelion root. Pour 3 cups of cold water over 3 teaspoonfuls of the mixture in the evening; in the morning bring to the boil, leave to cool and then strain. Drink one cup 3 times a day.

24

100g   Nettle herbage

One teaspoonful of the drug for one cup of the infusion. Drink 3 times a day. A decoction can also be prepared from 2-2½ teaspoonfuls of the leaves to 2 cups of water; boil gently 5 minutes, strain into a vacuum flask and drink ½ cup 2-3 times a day.

ANTISCLEROTIC MIXTURES

Basic drugs: flower, fruit and leaf of Hawthorn — herbage of Balm — herbage of Rue — herbage of Mistletoe — Garlic.

Examples of herbal mixtures:

10 parts	Carraway seeds	15 parts	Valerian root
10 parts	Rue leaf	25 parts	Hawthorn flower
15 parts	Balm leaf	25 parts	Mistletoe herbage

One tablespoonful of the mixture to a cup of water; bring to the boil and then leave to macerate overnight. Drink one cup 3 times a day.

25g	Garlic	25g	Horse-tail herbage
25g	Hawthorn	25g	Mistletoe

One tablespoonful of the mixture to one cup of decoction. Drink one cup morning and evening.

For sclerosis and high blood pressure:

25g	Mistletoe herbage	20g	Hawthorn leaf
25g	Rue herbage	10g	Shepherd's Purse herbage
20g	Horse-tail herbage		

An infusion of a tablespoonful of the mixture to a cup of water. Drink one cup 3 times a day.

20g	Mistletoe herbage	15g	Rue herbage
20g	Horse-tail herbage	15g	Yarrow herbage
20g	Shepherd's Purse herbage	15g	Dandelion root
		15g	Centaury herbage

One tablespoonful of the mixture for one cup of the infusion. Drink one cup in the evening.

50g   Mistletoe herbage

One tablespoonful to a cup of cold water; leave to macerate about 8 hours overnight. Drink in the course of the day.

50g	Nettle leaf	20g	Peppermint leaf
30g	Licorice root	20g	Blackthorn flower
30g	St. John's Wort herbage	20g	Heartsease
		20g	Dandelion root
30g	Ribbed Melilot	20g	Dandelion flower

A decoction of two teaspoonfuls of the herbal mixture to 2 cups of water; cover and boil 3 minutes, leave to stand 5 minutes, strain into a thermos flask. Drink ½ cup 2-3 times a day.

DIURETIC MIXTURES for the disinfection of the urinary tract.
Basic drugs: Birch leaf — Bearberry leaf — Juniper berries — Prickly Restharrow root.

Examples of herbal mixtures:

20g	Horse-tail herbage	20g	Bearberry leaf
35g	Birch leaf	25g	Chicory root

A decoction of 3 teaspoonfuls of the mixtures to 3½ glasses of water; cover and heat 3-5 minutes, leave to stand 5-10 minutes, then strain into a vacuum flask. Drink in doses of ⅔-1 glass 3-4 times a day between meals.

10g	Prickly Restharrow root	10g	Yarrow
10g	Juniper berries (crushed)	20g	Horse-tail herbage
		30g	Birch leaf
10g	Nettle herbage	10g	Golden Rod herbage

One teaspoonful of the mixture for one cup of the infusion. Drink lukewarm twice a day.

20g	Yarrow herbage	20g	Valerian root
20g	St. John's Wort herbage	25g	Ling herbage
15g	Peppermint leaf		

One teaspoonful for a cup of the infusion. Drink lukewarm 2-3 times a day.

Equal quantities of Rupture-Wort herbage, Bearberry leaf, Flax seed and Angelica root.
One teaspoonful of the mixture for a cup of the infusion. Drink several cups a day.

10g	Marsh Mallow root	10g	Oak bark
10g	Flax seed	20g	Bearberry leaf
30g	Balm leaf		

One teaspoonful of the mixture to one cup of cold water; macerate 8 hours, then pour off half the liquid and bring the remaining half to the boil. After straining mix with the first half and drink.

10g	Flax seed	20g	Birch leaf
10g	Bogbean leaf	30g	Bearberry leaf
10g	Licorice root		

One teaspoonful of the mixture to one cup of cold water; macerate 3 hours, then bring to the boil, leave to stand 15 minutes, strain and drink.

EXPECTORANT MIXTURES to loosen, relieve a cough.

Basic drugs: Cowslip root and flower (saponin drugs in general) — to suppress a cough: Mallow leaf and flower — Marsh Mallow leaf and root (drugs containing mucilage in general).

Examples of herbal mixtures:

Equal quantities in weight of Coltsfoot leaf, Plaintain leaf, Mullein and Mallow flowers.

One teaspoonful of the mixture for one cup of the infusion (preferably combine maceration and infusion). Drink hot, 2-3 cups a day.

20g	Fennel seed	15g	Elderberry flower
20g	Common Speedwell herbage	15g	Coltsfoot leaf
		10g	Sweet Violet root
20g	Soapwort or Cowslip root		

One tablespoon for a cup of decoction. Drink hot several times a day.

A decoction of Soapwort root (10g to 180ml water); strain and add 200g of syrup from Marsh Mallow root (buy at the pharmacist's). Drink one tablespoonful every 3 hours.

Equal quantities in weight of Elderberry flower, Linden flower, Chamomile inflorescence, Mullein and Cowslip flowers.

One tablespoonful of the herbal mixture for one cup of decoction. Drink hot, one cup 3 times a day.

Equal quantities in weight of Burnet Saxifrage root, Thyme herbage, St. John's Wort herbage, Nettle and Plantain leaves.

One tablespoonful for a cup of decoction. Drink hot, one cup several times a day.

Equal quantities in weight of Licorice root, Coltsfoot leaf, Marsh Mallow root and Plantain leaf.

One tablespoonful for a cup of decoction. Drink one cup 3-5 times a day.

Equal parts of Mullein and Mallow flowers.

One tablespoonful for a cup of infusion. Drink hot, one cup several times a day.

METABOLIC MIXTURES 'purifying the blood'

Basic drugs: diuretics, laxatives and amatotonics in general.

Examples of herbal mixtures:

20g	Yarrow herbage	20g	Valerian root
20g	St. John's Wort herbage	25g	Ling herbage
15g	Peppermint leaf		

One tablespoonful of the mixture for a cup of infusion. Drink one cup before going to bed.

50g	Blackthorn flower	10g	Peppermint herbage
20g	Dandelion root	10g	Elderberries
10g	Caraway seed		

One tablespoonful of the mixture for a glass of infusion. Drink before going to bed or once a day. This herbal mixture is suitable for slimming.

50g	Ling flower	50g	Lady's Mantle
5g	Wormwood herbage		

One tablespoonful for one cup of infusion. Drink before going to bed.

LAXATIVE MIXTURES

Basic drugs: Flax seeds, Blackthorn flower.

Examples of herbal mixtures:
1. Two teaspoonfuls of the drug to a glass of water; macerate 8 hours. Drink in the course of the day.
2. One teaspoonful of the drug for a cup of infusion. Drink hot morning and evening.

50g Berry-bearing Alder bark (Alder Buckthorn, Black Dogwood, *(Fragula alnus)*

20g	Dandelion root	10g	Caraway seed
10g	Peppermint herbage	10g	Elderberries

One tablespoonful of the herbal mixture for a glass of the infusion. Drink before going to bed or once a day — preferably lukewarm in the evening.

25g	Berry-bearing Alder bark	20g	Balm herbage
30g	Comfrey root	10g	Fennel seed
20g	Yarrow herbage		

Two teaspoonfuls of the mixture to 2 cups of water; leave to macerate 10 hours. Drink one cup every morning.

40g	Berry-bearing Alder bark	20g	Lime flower
10g	Fennel seed	20g	Elderberry flower

An infusion of one tablespoonful of the herbal mixture to ¼ litre of water. Drink lukewarm, one cup in the evening.

NERVINE MIXTURES — SEDATIVES

Basic drugs: Lavender flower — Balm leaf — Hop cones — Marjoram herbage — Valerian root.

Examples of herbal teas:

40g	Valerian root	15g	Balm herbage
10g	Chamomile inflorescence	15g	Peppermint herbage
20g	Yarrow		

One tablespoonful of the mixture for a cup of infusion. Drink on an empty stomach in the morning and before going to bed (as an antispasmodic and hypnotic as well).

10g	Fennel seed	20g	Balm leaf
20g	Chamomile inflorescence	5g	Marjoram herbage
10g	Peppermint leaf		

An infusion of one tablespoonful of the mixture to a glass of water. Drink 2-3 cups a day. This herbal mixture calms an upset stomach very effectively. It can be sweetened with honey.

GASTRIC AND BITTER MIXTURES (in cases of insufficient gastric juices — hypoacidity)

Basic drugs: Bogbean leaf — Angelica root — Gentian root — Sweet Flag root (rhizome) — Saxifrage root

Equal quantities in weight of Sweet Flag root (rhizome), Caraway seed, Coriander seed, St. John's Wort herbage, Angelica root and Centaury herbage.

A macerated decoction of one teaspoonful to one tablespoonful of the drug. Drink 2-3 cups a day.

NOTE: Drugs mentioned above which are not included in the pictorial section can be bought at a pharmacy.

A list of medical plants classified according to their therapeutic uses.

ADSTRINGENS — an astringent agent
Agrimony — Lady's Mantle — Bearberry — Large-flowered Sticky Eyebright — Wild Strawberry — Hemp-Nettle — Herb Bennet — Ground Ivy — St. John's Wort — Hyssop — White Dead-Nettle — Common Knotgrass — Silverweed — Blackthorn — Lungwort — Common Oak — Blackberry — Raspberry — Summer Savory — Golden Rod — Garden Thyme — Coltsfoot — Bilberry — Cowberry — Vervain.

ADVULNANS — for external use on wounds
St. John's Wort — Ribbed Melilot — Comfrey.

AMARO-AROMATICUM — aromatic, bitter substances
Wormwood.

AMARUM — bitter substances — see STOMACHICUM (encourages the production of gastric juices) and TONICUM (an invigorating, strengthening agent)

ANAESTETICUM — an insensitizing agent (anaesthetic)
Peppermint.

ANALGETICUM — a pain killer
Henbane — Opium Poppy (extracts) — Elderberry.

ANAPHRODISIACUM — diminishing sexual desire
Hop.

ANGIOTONICUM — improving vascular tone.
Hawthorn — Ribbed Melilot.

ANTHELMINTICUM — against internal parasites
Garden Thyme.

ANTIARTHRITICUM — for arthritis
Autumn Crocus (extract).

ANTIARYTHMICUM — regulating the beating of the heart
Mistletoe.

ANTIASTHMATICUM — for asthma
Large-flowered Sticky Eyebright.

ANTIBECHICUM — suppressing a cough
Opium Poppy (extracts) — Garden Thyme.

ANTICOAGULANS — preventing coagulation of the blood
Ribbed Melilot.

ANTIDIABETICUM — for diabetes
Goat's Rue — Common Sage — Bilberry.

ANTIDIARRHOICUM — for diarrhoea
Herb Bennet — Opium Poppy (extracts) — Silverweed — Blackthorn — Common Oak — Blackcurrant — Blackberry — Stinging Nettle.

ANTIHAEMORRHAGICUM — against excess menstrual bleeding
White Dead-Nettle.

ANTIHYDROTICUM — antiperspirant (see ANTISUDORIFICUM)
ANTIMITOTICUM — limiting cell division (mitosis)
  Autumn Crocus.
ANTINEURALGICUM — against neurotic pain
  Vervain.
ANTIODEMATICUM — for edemata (swellings)
  Horse Chestnut.
ANTIPEDICULOSUM — against lice
  Tansy.
ANTIPHILOGISTICUM — for inflammations
  Yarrow — Horse Chestnut — Agrimony — Arnica — Borage — Large-
  flowered Sticky Eyebright — Ground Ivy — Licorice — Common
  Toadflax — Common Mallow — Chamomile — Ribwort Plantain —
  Blackthorn — Lungwort — Blackberry — Common Sage — Soapwort
  — Golden Rod — Comfrey.
ANTISCLEROTICUM — for sclerosis
  Horse-tail — Mistletoe.
ANTISCORBUTICUM — against scurvy, bleeding of the gums.
  Dog Rose.
ANTISEPTICUM — antiseptic agent — germ killer
  Wormwood — Hop — Common Juniper — Peppermint — Sweet
  Basil — Wild Marjoram — Blackcurrant — Common Sage — Summer
  Savory — Wild Thyme — Garden Thyme — Stinging Nettle —
  Bilberry — Common Speedwell.
ANTISPASMODICUM — for spasms (of the smooth muscle of special areas
  — otherwise see SPASMOLYTICUM — more universally effective)
  Arnica — Wormwood — Deadly Nightshade (extracts) — Henbane
  (extracts) — Chamomile — Balm — Peppermint — Opium Poppy
  (extracts).
ANTISUDORIFICUM — preventing excessive perspiration
  Hyssop — Common Sage.
ANTIURATICUM — preventing the forming of deposits of urates (salt of uric
acid) in gout
  Autumn Crocus (extracts).
AROMATICUM — aromatic, fragrant substances
  Angelica — Sweet Basil — Wild Thyme — Garden Thyme.
BACTERISTATICUM — specially for baths
  Chamomile.
CARDIOTONICUM (CARDIACUM) — heart tonic improving heart muscle tone
  Lily-of-the-Valley — Hawthorn — Foxglove — Motherwort.
CARMINATIVUM — for flatulence
  Yarrow — Angelica — Coriander — Fennel — Common Juniper —
  Chamomile — Ribbed Melilot — Peppermint — Sweet Basil — Wild
  Marjoram — Summer Savory.
CHOLAGOGUM — increases the flow of bile
  Agrimony — Wormwood — Greater Celandine — Chicory — Yellow
  Gentian — Common Juniper — Common Toadflax — Peppermint —

31

Bogbean — Silverweed — Dog Rose — Raspberry — Rue — Dandelion — Broad-leaved Lime.

CHOLERETICUM — increasing the production of bile
Fumitory.

CONSPERGENS — for sprinkling (against stickiness, etc.)
Club Moss (Lycopodium).

CORRIGENS — improving taste, smell
Coriander — Fennel — Licorice.

DEPURATIVUM (see METABOLICUM) 'purifying the blood' — influencing the metabolic processes in the organism

DERIVANS — improving the blood supply to the skin
Arnica — Common Juniper — Rosemary — Stinging Nettle.

DERMATOLOGICUM — skin cosmetic
Flax (oil) — Chamomile — Common Sage — Broad-leaved Lime.

DESINFICIENS — killing germs (see also URODESINFICIENS)
Bearberry — Silver Birch — Horse-tail — Herb Bennet — Prickly Restharrow — Burnet Saxifrage — Bilberry.

DETERGENS — for external use, for cleaning and healing wounds
Ribbed Melilot.

DIAPHORETICUM — to provoke sweating
Silver Birch — Ling — Goat's Rue — Chamomile — Wild Marjoram — Cowslip — Blackthorn — Blackcurrant — Raspberry — Elderberry — Broad-leaved Lime — Vervain — Heartsease.

DIETETICUM — for dieting
Chicory (inulin) — Common Oak (acorns) — Raspberry (fruit) — Cowberry (fruit).

DIURETICUM — increasing the volume of urine excreted (see also SALUTERICUM)
Bearberry — Wormwood — Silver Birch — Borage — Ling — Shepherd's Purse — Chicory — Lily-of-the-Valley — Hawthorn — Foxglove — Horse-tail — Wild Strawberry — Fumitory — Goat's Rue — Hemp-Nettle — Ground Ivy — Licorice — Rupture-wort — St. John's Wort — Common Juniper — Common Toadflax — Club Moss — Ribbed Melilot — Spiny Restharrow — Wild Marjoram — Burnet Saxifrage — Common Knotgrass — Cowslip — Blackthorn — Lungwort — Blackcurrant — Dog Rose — Blackberry — Raspberry — Rue — Elderberry — Golden Rod — Dandelion — Broad-leaved Lime — Stinging Nettle — Bilberry — Vervain — Heartsease.

EMMENAGOGUM — regulating menstruation
Wormwood — Rue — Common Sage.

EMOLLIENS — a softening agent
Marsh Mallow — Borage — Common Toadflax — Flax — Common Mallow.

EXPECTORANS — to loosen a cough
Fennel — Hemp-Nettle — Ground Ivy — Licorice — Hyssop — Common Juniper — White Dead-Nettle — Burnet Saxifrage —

Ribwort Plantain — Cowslip — Lungwort — Soapwort — Wild Thyme — Garden Thyme — Common Speedwell — Sweet Violet — Heartsease.

GALACTAGOGUM (See LACTAGOGUM) — to increase the flow of milk

HAEMOSTATICUM — for bleeding
Yarrow — Horse Chestnut — Horse-tail.

HAEMOSTYPTICUM — to stop bleeding
Shepherd's Purse — Common Knotgrass — Silverweed — Stinging Nettle.

HYPOTENSIVUM — for high blood pressure (=HYPOTONICUM)
Motherwort — Mistletoe.

LACTAGOGUM — to increase the flow of milk
Fennel — Goat's Rue — Vervain.

LAXANS — a laxative
Marsh Mallow — Common Toadflax — Flax — Blackthorn — Elderberry.

METABOLICUM — stimulating metabolic processes
Lady's Mantle — Silver Birch — Ling — Chicory — Wild Strawberry — Fumitory — Ground Ivy — Bogbean — Spring Restharrow — Wild Marjoram — Burnet Saxifrage — Common Knotgrass — Cowslip — Blackberry — Raspberry — Soapwort — Dandelion — Stinging Nettle — Common Speedwell — Heartsease — Mistletoe.

MUCILAGINOSUM — forming a protective film of mucus
White Dead-Nettle — Common Mallow — Ripwort Plantain — Lungwort — Comfrey — Coltsfoot.

MYDRIATICUM — to dilate the pupil of the eye
Deadly Nightshade.

NARCOTICUM — to numb the senses
Opium Poppy (extract).

NERVINUM — to soothe the nerves
Coriander — Balm — Rosemary — Sweet Violet.

NUTRIENS — a nutrative substance
Flax (oil).

PARASYMPATICOLYTICUM — to influence certain areas of the intestinal smooth muscle, suppress the secretion of various organs, etc.
Deadly Nightshade — Henbane.

PROTECTIVUM — to form a protective layer, thus preventing irritation
Marsh Mallow — Borage — Flax — Common Mallow — Comfrey.

SALUTERICUM — encouraging the excretion from the organism of various salts
Bearberry — Cowberry.

SECRETOLYTICUM — to dissolve mucus, dilute secretions
Wild Marjoram — Burnet Saxifrage — Soapwort — Sweet Violet.

SEDATIVUM — a calming, soothing agent
Angelica — Ling — Greater Celandine — Hop — St. John's Wort — White Dead-Nettle — Motherwort — Balm — Opium Poppy — Rue — Broad-leaved Lime — Valerian.

SPASMOLYTICUM — to relieve spasms in general and of the smooth muscle in particular

Yarrow — Lady's Mantle — Greater Celandine — Coriander — Hawthorn — Licorice — Rupture-wort — St. John's Wort — Ribbed Melilot — Wild Marjoram — Burnet Saxifrage — Silverweed — Rosemary — Rue — Broad-leaved Lime — Coltsfoot — Valerian.

STIMULANS — a stimulating agent

Rosemary.

STOMACHICUM — stimulating the production of gastric juices

Agrimony — Lady's Mantle — Angelica — Wormwood — Ling — Centaury — Chicory — Coriander — Large-flowered Sticky Eyebright — Fennel — Fumitory — Hemp-Nettle — Yellow Gentian — Herb Bennet — Ground Ivy — Hop — St. John's Wort — Hyssop — Common Juniper — Motherwort — Balm — Peppermint — Bogbean — Sweet Basil — Spiny Restharrow — Wild Marjoram — Burnet Saxifrage — Ribwort Plantain — Silverweed — Rue — Common Sage — Summer Savory — Dandelion — Wild Thyme — Garden Thyme — Broad-leaved Lime — Common Speedwell.

TONICUM — an invigorating and strengthening agent

Wormwood — Centaury — Chicory — Yellow Gentian — Bogbean — Dog Rose — Rosemary — Common Speedwell — Heartsease.

URODESIFICIENS — for disinfecting the urinary tract (see also DESINFICIENS)

Bearberry — Ling — Rupture-wort — Club Moss — Cowberry.

UTEROTONICUM — mitigating contractions of the womb

Shepherd's Purse — Rue.

VASOTONICUM — to increase vascular tension

Horse-Chestnut — Arnica.

VEHICULUM — auxiliary substance facilitating the absorption of medicines

Flax (oil).

VERMIFUGUM — to expel worms, internal parasites

Wormwood — Tansy.

The 88 medicinal plants included in the book, with their botanical and common English names:

Achillea millefolium — Yarrow
Aesculus hippocastanum — Horse Chestnut
Agrimonia eupatoria — Agrimony
Alchemilla vulgaris — Lady's Mantle
Althaea officinalis — Marsh Mallow
Angelica archangelica — Angelica
Arctostaphylos uva-ursi — Alpine Bearberry
Arnica montana — Arnica
Artemisia absinthium — Wormwood
Atropa bella-donna — Deadly Nightshade, Belladonna
Betula pendula (verrucosa) — Silver Birch
Borago officinalis — Borage
Calluna vulgaris — Ling, Heather
Capsella bursa-pastoris — Shepherd's Purse
Centaurium minus (*C. umbellatum*) — Centaury
Chelidonium majus — Greater Celandine
Cichorium intybus — Chicory
Colchicum autumnale — Meadow Saffron, Autumn Crocus
Convallaria majalis — Lily-of-the-Valley
Coriandrum sativum — Coriander
Crataegus oxycanthoides (oxyacantha) — Wood Hawthorn, Midland Hawthorn
Digitalis purpurea — Foxglove
Equisetum arvense — Common Horse-tail
Euphrasia rostkoviana (officinalis) — Large-flowered Sticky Eyebright
Foeniculum vulgare — Fennel
Fragaria vesca — Wild Strawberry
Fumaria officinalis — Common Fumitory
Galega officinalis — Goat's Rue
Galeopsis segetum — Downy Hemp-nettle
Gentiana lutea — Great Yellow Gentian
Geum urbanum — Herb Bennet, Wood Avens
Glechoma hederacea — Ground Ivy, Field Balm
Glycyrrhiza glabra — Licorice
Herniaria glabra — Smooth Rupturewort
Humulus lupulus — Hop
Hypericum perforatum — Perforate St. John's Wort
Hyssopus officinalis — Hyssop
Juniperus communis — Common Juniper
Lamium album — White Dead-nettle
Leonurus cardiaca — Motherwort
Linaria vulgaris — Common Toadflax
Linum usitatissimum — Common Flax

Lycopodium clavatum — Stagshorn Clubmoss
Malva sylvestris — Common Mallow
Matricaria chamomilla (recutita) — Scented Mayweed, Wild Chamomile
Melilotus officinalis — Ribbed Melilot
Melissa officinalis — Balm (Lemon Balm)
Mentha × piperita — Peppermint
Menyanthes trifoliata — Bogbean, Buck-bean
Ocimum basilicum — Sweet Basil
Ononis spinosa — Spiny Restharrow
Origanum vulgare — Wild Marjoram, Oregano
Papaver somniferum — Opium Poppy
Pimpinella saxifraga — Burnet Saxifrage
Plantago lanceolata — Ripwort Plantain
Polygonum aviculare — Common Knotgrass
Potentilla anserina — Silverweed
Primula veris (officinalis) — Cowslip
Prunus spinosa — Blackthorn, Sloe
Pulmonaria officinalis — Lungwort
Quercus robur — Common Oak, English Oak
Ribes nigrum — Blackcurrant
Rosa canina — Dog Rose
Rosmarinus officinalis — Rosemary
Rubus fruticosus — Blackberry, Bramble
Rubus idaeus — Raspberry
Ruta graveolens — Rue
Salvia officinalis — Common Sage, Garden Sage
Sambucus nigra — Common Elder
Saponaria officinalis — Soapwort
Satureia hortensis — Summer Savory
Solidago virgaurea — Golden Rod
Symphytum officinalis — Common Comfrey
Tanacetum vulgare — Tansy
Taraxacum officinale — Dandelion
Thymus serpyllum — Wild Thyme
Thymus vulgaris — Garden Thyme
Tilia platyphyllos — Broad-leaved lime, Linden
Tussilago farfara — Coltsfoot
Urtica dioica — Stinging Nettle
Vaccinium myrtillus — Bilberry, Blueberry, Whortleberry
Vaccinium vitis-idaea — Cowberry
Valeriana officinalis — Common Valerian
Verbena officinalis — Vervain
Veronica officinalis — Common Speedwell, Heath Speedwell
Viola odorata — Sweet Violet
Viola tricolor — Heartsease, Wild Pansy
Viscum album — Mistletoe

THE PLANTS

Symbols

*	annual herb
†	biennial herb
‡	perennial herb
* *	semi-shrub
††	shrub
‡‡	tree

Note: (+) = Warning
    + = Poisonous plant

YARROW

15-30cm (6-12in) — ‡
Flowers: June-October

Achillea millefolium
Asteraceae (Compositae)
Flores Millefolii — flower (inflorescence), *Herba Millefolii* — herbage

Botanical description	Erect stalk, branching at the top. Alternate, tripinnate leaves. Capitulatum of tiny sessile flowers in corymb formation.
Habitat	Sandy and barren places, meadows, by the wayside, throughout the northern hemisphere.
Collection	Cut off the flowering top parts with very short stalks at the beginning of the flowering period. In the case of herbage, collect only the succulent parts (stalk and leaves).
Drying	Dry quickly, in the shade. Artificial heat must not exceed 35°-40°C (95°-104°F).
Cultivation	Does not require good soil, but likes nitrogen.
Active constituents	Above all silica, and the chamazulene and furocoumarins in it, flavones, bitter principles, tannins and a considerable amount of mineral salts.
Efficacy	Haemostaticum, spasmolyticum, carminativum, anti-phlogisticum.
Use	Internal bleeding in the alimentary canal, haemorrhoids, gastric and intestinal ulcers. Antispasmodic effect on the smooth muscle — in popular medicine used also for angina pectoris. Generally for spasms of the urinary tract, bladder and alimentary canal; for habitual constipation, loss of appetite, indigestion, flatulence. Externally it is applied to inflammations and used for compresses and baths.
Dosage	Usually as an infusion with 2 tablespoonfuls of the drug to 0.25-0.5 litre (8½-17oz) of water, unsweetened, ½-1 glass 2-3 times a day. For external use, double quantities of the drug. Efficacy similar to that of Chamomile. However, these drugs are not used by themselves; for the most part they are combined as auxiliary drugs in antisclerotic, metabolic and gastric infusions, and with those prescribed to stimulate the excretion of bile.
Warning	Do not increase the doses unnecessarily, because the juice of the plant can cause dermatitis. It is recommended to collect specimens with white flowers only.

HORSE CHESTNUT

30m or more (100ft) — ‡‡
Flowers: April-June

Aesculus hippocastanum
Aesculaceae

Flores Hippocastani — flower; *Semen Hippocastani* — seed; *Folia Hippocastani* — leaf; *Cortex Hippocastani* — bark; *Pericarpium Hippocastani* — pericarp

Botanical description	Tree with a thick crown. Large digitate leaves (5-7 leaflets on long petioles). White flowers arranged in upright conical clusters.
Habitat	Grown singly or in avenues.
Cultivation	Prefers sheltered, sunny sites and deep, permeable soil.
Collection	The bark in the spring, the leaf when young, the flower at the beginning of the flowering season and the seed (chestnut) and pericarp when mature.
Drying	The flower is sensitive to drying. Artificial heat at 35°-40°C (95°-104°F) produces the best results. Other parts in the usual way.
Active constituents	The therapeutically active constituents are saponins, especially aesculin, flavones and coumarins.
Efficacy	Vasotonicum, antioedamaticum, haemostaticum, antiphlogisticum.
Use	The combined effect of the saporins and flavones is important for the regulation of the blood circulation, having anticoagulant properties and strengthening the vascular walls; anti-oedematous effect.
	Aesculin is an important factor and it is therefore extracted for industrial use in pharmaceutical preparations.
Dosage	According to popular tradition, a decoction of pericarps (5 per cent), 2-3 cups a day (for anal fissures, haemorrhoids, hypertrophy of the prostate gland). Decoction of one teaspoonful of the bark to 1-2 glasses of water, ⅓-½ glass drunk 2-3 times a day 10-15 minutes before meals. Decoction of one teaspoonful of the flower to 2 glasses of water, ½ glass taken 3 times a day (30 minutes before meals) but usually only used externally. As a popular medicine an infusion of 2-3 teaspoonfuls to one glass is also recommended for inflammations of the upper respiratory passages. Apart from providing extracts extracts of certain active principles, the seeds are also used as animal fodder. A pinch of dried seed in spirits is popularly used as an antidiarrhoicum.

AGRIMONY

30-130cm (12-50in) — ‡
Flowers: June-August

Agrimonia eupatoria
Rosaceae
Herba Agrimoniae — herbage

Botanical description	A hairy herb with an erect stem terminated by spikes of small yellow flowers. The petiolated, alternate leaves on the lower part of the stem are pinnate with lanceolate, serrate leaflets.
Habitat	Grows in semi-dry meadows, by the wayside, in sunny woodland clearings. It likes warmth.
Collection	The flowering herbage of second-year plants is collected and supplemented by leaves cut off separately.
Drying	Dry in a well-aired, shady place. If artificial heat is used, it should not exceed 35°C (95°F).
Cultivation	Requires loamy to sandy or medium, stony soil. Sow by hand in autumn, 4-6 seeds in shallow holes in a grid pattern 60×60cm (2ft×2ft) apart. The seeds must be covered with soil.
Active constituents	The therapeutically active substances are tannins (5-8 per cent), bitter principles, silica, mineral salts, flavones and nicotinamides.
Efficacy	Cholagogum, adstringens, amarum, antiphlogisticum.
Use	For gastric and intestinal ulcers, inflammation of the gall-bladder (usually in combination with the herbage of Wormwood and Celandine, Peppermint leaf and Dandelion root), also for diarrhoea, digestive disorders, insufficiency of gastric juices, slight internal bleeding resulting from damaged capillaries, mild food poisoning (especially in children). Externally it is used for compresses, swabs, gargles, applied to wounds, skin rashes, inflammation of the veins (varicose veins) — here in combination with Comfrey — for throat inflammations, and so on.
Dosage	Infusion of the herbage (10-50g to 500ml (17oz) water) in ½ glass 2-3 times a day; decoction (25-50g to 500ml (17oz) water), boil 15 minutes — as a gargle add a teaspoonful of honey and glycerine. For external usage 40-60g of the drug to 500ml of water. The drug is frequently a component of herbal teas for disorders of the gall bladder.
Warning	Stalks over 5mm (¹/₅in) thick and the fruit reduces the value of the drug.

LADY'S MANTLE

Alchemilla vulgaris
Rosaceae
Herba Alchemillae — herbage

15-50cm (6-20in) — ‡
Flowers: May-October

Botanical description	Polymorphic herb — radical, fan-like leaves palmately pinnatilobate with 7-11 lobes, usually serrate. Drops of water can be found at the edges and in the centre of the leaves in the morning. Tiny clusters of terminal flowers.
Habitat	Abundant in fields, meadows, by the roadside, on banks and elsewhere.
Collection	The flowering herbage with radical leaves.
Drying	Quickly, at natural temperatures; artificial heat up to 30°-35°C (85°-95°F).
Cultivation	Prefers loose, deep, dampish soils. Not fond of lime.
Active constituents	Chiefly tannins, organic acids and mineral salts.
Efficacy	Adstringens, stomachicum, spasmolyticum, metabolicum (depurativum).
Use	Mildly astringent effect of the mucous membrane; slow down the development of microorganisms and prevents excessive fermentation. Slightly increases the secretion of gastric juices, facilitates the absorption and digestion of food. Used for unspecified catarrhs of the stomach and intestines, flatulence, insufficient secretion of gastric juices. Externally, for compresses, swabs and gargles (for conjuctivitis in combination with Chamomile flower heads and Large-flowered Sticky Eyebright herbage).
Dosage	Infusion (10-25g of the drug to 500ml water) ⅓-½ glass, 2-3 times a day between meals. The same for external use. Rarely used alone — combined with drugs containing tannins, bitter principles or silica.
Note	This is a very popular drug. The *Alchemilla* genus is very large and botanical identification is extremely difficult.

MARSH MALLOW

Althaea officinalis
Malvaceae

80-120cm (2ft 6in-4ft) — ‡
Flowers: June-September

Radix Althaeae — root; *Folia Althaeae* — leaf; *Flores Althaeae* — flower;
Herba Althaeae — herbage

Botanical description	Covered with velvety down throughout. Erect stem, slightly branching; alternate leaves with 3-5 lobes and irregular, dentate edges. The large flowers form a sparse terminal raceme.
Habitat	Grows mainly in salt marshes.
Collection	The root is dug up in autumn and the corky layer is usually peeled off. The leaf is collected before the flowering period. The herbage is collected in the same period as the leaf, and the flower when opening.
Drying	Dry the root by artificial heat up to 45°C (113°F), the leaf in thin layers at natural temperatures.
Cultivation	For collection of the leaf, sow the seeds in autumn (September) or early in the spring. To achieve thick roots loamy to sandy soil with sufficient ground water is needed. The plant is grown either from the shoots at the top of the roots or from seeds.
Active constituents	Mucilage, starch, sugars, pectins, mineral salts, a small quantity of tannins and asparagine.
Efficacy	Protectivum, emolliens, laxans.
Use	Medicine for catarrh of the respiratory and alimentary tracts, protective and softening medicament for irritation. Macerations have proved their worth for inflammations of the throat and mouth as well as for coughs. Gentle laxative.
Dosage	As a laxative 2-4g of powdered root 2-3 times a day. For the respiratory tract make a maceration of one teaspoonful of chopped root to a glass of water at room temperature; leave to stand for 30 minutes and strain; drink ¼-⅓glass 2-3 times a day. As an expectorant it is combined with other herbs. It can also be used externally as an antiphlogistic for infants. The leaf is usually decocted (1-2 per cent); the effect is more moderate, but it is not a laxative, the usual dosage being 1½ teaspoonfuls to 1-1½ glasses of water; used internally, or externally for compresses. The flower is slightly mucilganinous.

ANGELICA

Angelica archangelica
Daucaceae (Apiaceae, Umbelliferae)
Radix Angelicae — root; *Fructus Angelicae* — fruit

50-250cm (20in-8ft) — †
Flowers: June-July

Botanical description	Hollow, grooved stem. Lower leaves doubly pinnate; upper leaves pinnate; large sheaths. Tiny greenish-white flowers in compound umbels. Fruit: carpophore.
Habitat	Grows in meadows at fairly high altitudes, especially along the banks of streams.
Collection	The root is dug up in the autumn in its second year. The fruit is collected before maturing (September).
Drying	Dry by artificual heat at 30°-35°C (85°-95°F); the drugs easily become damp and the root is particularly susceptible to parasites.
Cultivation	A plant preferring damp, semi-heavy soils, deeply cultivated and rich in humus. The seed is first sown in a hotbed, the seedlings then planted out 40×50cm (15×20in) apart.
Active constituents	The main therapeutically active principles are flavones and silica, containing terpenes, sesquiterpenes and furocoumarins.
Efficacy	Aromaticum, amarum, stomachicum, carminativum, sedativum.
Use	Considerably increases the secretion of gastric juices, to a lesser extent diuresis and perspiration; it can cause an increase in menstrual flow. Effective against spasms, slightly increases the peristalsis of the intestines. Suitable for loss of appetite from nervous causes, inflammations and spasms of the small intestine, for atony of the intestines, flatulence (often applied in combination with Fennel, Caraway, Anise, etc.). The tincture also has a beneficial effect (100g root macerated 14 days in 1 litre 70 per cent alcohol.
Dosage	The infusion is made from 5-15g of the drug to 500ml water; drink ½ glass before meals as a stomachic, after meals as a carminative. Soothing baths (infusion from 200g root), also suitable for gargling, etc. Dosage for the tincture: 20-30 drops 2-4 times a day.
Warning	The furocoumarins in the juice of the plant can produce unpleasant skin rashes.

ALPINE BEARBERRY

Arctostaphylos uva-ursi
Ericaceae
Folium uvae ursi — leaf

30-100cm (1-3ft) — ††
Flowers: March-July

Botanical description	Shrub with thin trailing stem, decumbent branches taking root. Leathery evergreen leaves about 6×12mm (1¼-1½in) in size. Flowers in tight clusters, pitcher-shaped corolla. Fruit: red berries.
Habitat	Fairly rare species found in coniferous forests at mountain to subalpine elevations in the northern hemisphere.
Collection	The leaf can be collected at almost any time of the year.
Drying	Must be dried quickly, in the sun or shade or by artificial heat not exceeding 55°C (130°F).
Cultivation	Fairly difficult — if at all, then as a semi-cultivar. Favours loose soil, rich in humus, acid at least on the surface. Sunny positions.
Active constituents	Phenolic glucosides (chiefly arbutin), flavones, tannins and triterpenic substances.
Efficacy	Desinficiens (urodesinficiens), diureticum, adstringens, salutericum.
Use	The phenolic glucosides act as a disinfectant primarily of the urinary tract in cases of alkaline urine (if the urine is acid, sodium bicarbonate is prescribed). The flavones have a moderately diuretic effect, but are more important for the excretion of salts (salutericum). The tannins are astringent and anti-inflammatory agents. Useful for urinary calculi.
Dosage	An infusion from a coarse powder of the leaves, 20g to 250ml of water; drink 1-1½ tablespoonfuls every 3 hours (as a disinfectant and salutericum; note: the urine turns green in colour — no need for alarm!). The leaf is a frequent diuretic and urologic component in herbal tea mixtures.
Warning	In many countries this is a protected plant. The drinking of large quantities of teas containing Alpine Bearberry can cause constipation (on account of the tannins present) or gastric irritation. For this reason the tea should not be taken over long periods.

ARNICA (MOUNTAIN ARNICA)

(+) *Arnica montana*
Asteraceae (Compositae)

30-60cm (1-2ft) — ‡
Flowers: June-August
Caution

Radix (Rhizoma) Arnicae — root (rhizome); *Flores Arnicae* — flower (inflorescence)

Botanical description	Plant with an oblique rhizome and entire, lanceolate, opposite leaves forming a basal rosette; large flowerheads terminating the branches.
Habitat	Grows at sub-mountain and mountain elevations. Indigenous to central and southern Europe. Rare, protected.
Collection	The rhizomes and roots are dug up in the autumn. The flowerheads are collected at the beginning of the flowering season.
Drying	Clean the roots and leave to dry in the sun. Dry the flowers in thin layers in the shade in a well-ventilated place.
Cultivation	Farès well in damp, peaty soils and in a cool climate. The seeds are sown at the end of summer; propagate vegetatively by cuttings from the rhizome.
Active constituents	Bitter principles, flavones, silica containing thymic acid, triterpenic substances, colouring matter (carotenes), organic acids and their esters, sulphurous compounds, non-saturated carbides and polyphenols.
Efficacy	Vasotonicum, antispasmodicum; externally: antiphlogisticum; derivans.
Use	Arnica influences the blood circulation, the coronary arteries, raises blood pressure and causes contractions of the uterus. Used externally for rheumatism, haematomas, cutaneous inflammations, ulcers, eczema and burns.
Dosage	For external use the tincture is usually used diluted with water at least 1:3, or with an infusion of Chamomile to which 3 per cent aluminium acetate is added for compresses.
Warning	Keep out of the reach of children!

WORMWOOD

(+) *Artemisia absinthium*
Asteraceae (Compositae)
Herba Absinthii — herbage

50-100cm (20-40in) — ‡
Flowers: July-September

Botanical description	A rosette of pinnate leaves on long petioles appears first, then leaves grow from the lower woody stem. Tiny hemispherical flowerheads form a large terminal panicle. Stem, leaves and bracts silky.
Habitat	Grows at lowland to foothill elevations in the temperate regions of Europe.
Collection	The flowering top parts and the leaves are collected separately and then combined.
Drying	Dry quickly in the shade, artificial heat not over 35°-40°C (95°-100°F). The drug easily becomes damp after drying!
Cultivation	Grown in warm positions on fertile, semi-heavy soils. Likes calcareous and nitrogenous soils. 'German' Wormwood is reproduced vegetatively, 'Russian' Wormwood by sowing the seeds in a seed-bed.
Active constituents	Silica, bitter principles (of the prochamazulene type), flavones, tannins and vitamins.
Efficacy	Amaro-aromaticum, stomachicum, tonicum, cholagogum, diureticum, emmenogogum, antispasmodicum, verifugum, antisepticum.
Use	Preparations from the drug are effective in cases of insufficient gastric juices; they stimulate the blood circulation in the pelvic region, increase the secretion of bile, and act as a disinfectant.
Dosage	An infusion of 1-2 teaspoonfuls of the drug to a cup of water is taken 2-3 times a day. Wine can also be made by maceration (2 teaspoonfuls of the drug to 1 litre of white wine, macerate 14 days); drink 2 teaspoonfuls before meals several days running. The herbage is also used in powder form, 2 to 3g at a time; this dose is also used to expel worms (vermifuge). The tincture (also available at a pharmacy): 10-30 drops in 100ml water, take 2-3 times a day, 30 minutes before meals (as a tonic); 20-60 drops 3 times a day in 50ml of water to increase the flow of bile.
Warning	The drug is not suitable for use over longer periods or in large quantities, or for pregnant women.

DEADLY NIGHTSHADE, BELLADONNA 15-150cm (20in-5ft)
— ‡

+ *Atropa belladonna*　　　　　　　　　　　**Flowers: June-July**
Solanaceae　　　　　　　　　　　　　　　　Poisonous Plant
+ *Folia Belladonnae* — leaf; + *Radix Belladonnae* — root

Botanical description	A tall, branching herb. Leaf: entire, elliptic, almost oval and pointed. Flower: bell-shaped corolla with a 5-lobed chalice. Fruit: black, shiny berry.
Habitat	In deciduous forests, especially in beech-woods, from hilly to subalpine elevations throughout Europe; cultivated in the United States.
Collection	Undamaged leaves in the flowering period. The roots are dug up in autumn, quickly washed and spread out to dry.
Drying	The leaf must be dried quickly, in a draught of air, in thin layers, in drying rooms at 70°-80°C (160°-180°F). The roots are best dried in drying rooms, also at 70°-80°C. The drugs easily become damp.
Cultivation	Deep soil (if cultivated for the root), well-nourished, loamy, rich in humus. Sunny sites. Seeds planted outside or in hotbeds; after wintering the seedlings are planted out 40×50cm (15×20in).
Active constituents	Very toxic alkaloids (L-hyoscyamine, atropin), coumarins, tannins, organic acids; the leaf also contains flavones, which are not found in the root.
Efficacy	Parasympaticolyticum, antispasmodicum, mydriaticum.
Use	The alkaloids are used in the treatment of Parkinson's disease (paralysis of the nervous system characterized by trembling limbs). Extracts are often prescribed (known as the Bulgarian drug). Therapeutic doses reduce the secretion of the glands and ease convulsions.
Dosage	To give an idea — the therapeutic dose for the leaf is only 30-100 *milli*grams taken once. Larger doses greatly reduce the secretion of various glands, dilate the pupils, provoke conditions of extreme irritation, followed by a deep, narcotic sleep which terminates in paralysis of the respiratory centre.
Warning	On account of its poisonous nature and specific effect, the drug and the substances isolated from it or extracts can only be prescribed by a doctor.

SILVER BIRCH

Betula pendula (verrucosa)
Betulaceae
Folio Betulae — leaf

6-18m (20-60ft) — ‡‡
Flowers: March-April

Botanical description	Trunk covered with silvery-white, pellicular bark; young, hanging twigs covered with resinous warts. The leaves have long, thing petioles and deltoid, doubly dentate blades. Dioecious flowers in the form of catkins.
Habitat	Commonly found in forests with poor soil in the northern hemisphere.
Collection	The young, sticky leaf is collected.
Drying	Dried well spread out at temperatures up to 35°C (95°F).
Cultivation	Planted along the roadside, in gardens, etc.
Active constituents	Chiefly flavones, tannins, saponins, silica, mineral salts and vitamin C.
Efficacy	Diureticum, diaphoreticum, metabolicum, desinficiens.
Use	A reliable diuretic — does not irritate the kidneys; metabolicum, mild diaphoretic and weak disinfectant.
Dosage	Usually drunk as an infusion (2 teaspoonfuls of the drug to a glass of water 3-4 times a day between meals) as a diuretic and diaphoretic, but most often mixed with other drugs. A component of herbal teas for fevers (with Willow bark, the flowers of Broad-leaved Lime, etc.), rheumatism and inflammation of the joints, as well as of diuretic teas. In some parts the burgeons (buds) are also collected. They slightly increase the flow of bile; together with the leaf they are added to baths for rheumatism, cutaneous inflammations, eczemas, etc.
Note	The leaf of a similar Birch, *Betula pubescens*, is equally effective.

BORAGE

20-80cm (8-32in) — *
Flowers: June-August

Borago officinalis
Boraginaceae
Flos Boraginis — flower; *Herba Boraginis* — herbage

Botanical description	Hardy, bristly plant with an erect, often branching stem. Large ovate leaves, entire or dentate. Flowers usually deep blue, only rarely white, in loose clusters on long peduncles.
Habitat	Originally from southrrn Europe. Grows in temperate lowland regions.
Collection	Flower and herbage, sometimes the leaf; collect at the beginning of the flowering season.
Drying	Dry with care in the shade in thin layers, well spread out; when artificial heat is used it should not exceed 35°-40°C (95°-104°F). As a vegetable it is eaten fresh.
Cultivation	Mainly in gardens. The seed is sown out where required at the beginning of April.
Active constituents	Rich in mucilages, then tannins and soluble silicates; contains choline, organic acids and mineral salts (large quantities of potassium). When fresh, it is rich in vitamin C.
Efficacy	Protectivum, diureticum, emolliens, antiphlogisticum.
Use	This plant has long been used as a spice. Its importance in medicine is not great because it has not yet been sufficiently studied. Its therapeutic effect lies mainly in the presence of mucilages, tannins, silicates and mineral salts; it has an anti-inflammatory influence (on the urinary tract, for inflammations of the mouth, catarrh of the respiratory passages and stomach, inflammations of the mucous membranes, etc.), and it increases the flow of urine. It has a generally metabolic effect. When used externally it has a soothing effect on ulcers, boils, spots, rashes, etc.
Dosage	An infusion: (10-30g of the herbage to 500ml of water) ⅓-½ glass 2-3 times a day. This drug is rarely used by itself.

LING, HEATHER

Calluna vulgaris
Ericaceae

10-50cm (4-20in) — ††
Flowers: June-September

Flores Calunae — flower; *Herba Callunae* — herbage

Botanical description	Broom-like evergreen shrub with numerous erect branches taking root. Minute alternate leaves. The little flowers, sometimes white in colour, grow along leafy spikes about 15cm (6in) long.
Habitat	Grows throughout Europe — especially on inferior soils up to mountain elevations. Often carpets large areas.
Collection	The flower or the whole of the flowering top parts are collected. Can be tied up in small bundles before drying.
Cultivation	Likes sandy, acid, non-calcareous soils exposed to the sun.
Active constituents	Flavones, tannins, mineral salts (e.g. potassium), silica, bitter substances — the glycoside arbutin is not always present.
Efficacy	Diureticum, urodesinficiens, stomachicum, sedativum, diaphoreticum, metabolicum.
Use	Long used in home remedies, but almost always in combination with other drugs.
Dosage	The infusion (flower: 10-15g to 2 glasses of water) is usually drunk 2-3 times a day, ⅓-½ a glass. Herbage in smaller doses (or brief 3 per cent infusion) 2-3 cups a day. In popular medicine the drug is used in cases of insomnia (especially the flower), chronic inflammations of the urinary tract, stones, rheumatism, mild diarrhoea and insufficient secretion of gastric juices. It relieves pain caused by peptic ulcers.. A spring herbal tea (short decoction or infusion of such quantities of the herbage or flower as are sufficient to give it a reddish colour) can be drunk over a long period of time without fear of side effects.

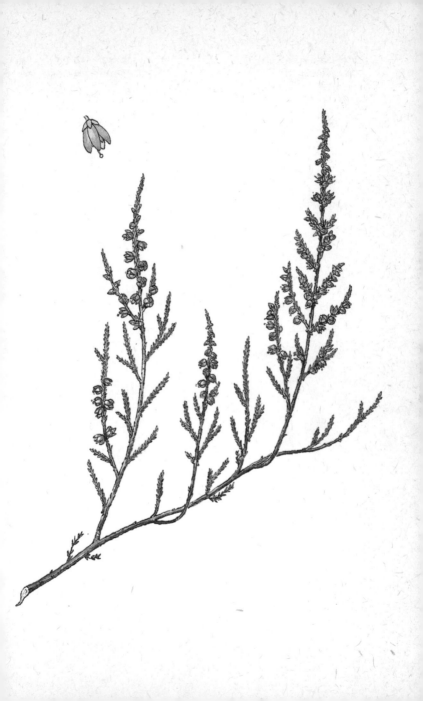

SHEPHERD'S PURSE

20-40cm (8-16in) — * — †
Flowers: March-October

Capsella bursa-pastoris
Brassicaceae (Cruciferae)
Herba Bursae pastoris — herbage

Botanical description	Herb with a rosette of basal leaves; the branching stem bears amplexicaul, lanceolate, pinnatifid leaves. The tiny flowers grow in terminal racemes and ripen into the characteristic triangular pods. A very variable herb.
Habitat	Nowadays a cosmopolitan species, a weed found on the most varied sites from lowland to mountain elevations.
Collection	Only clean, healthy, flowering herbage.
Drying	Dry quickly at natural temperatures.
Cultivation	Not necessary, abundant in places.
Active constituents	Biogenic amines (histamin, choline and others), flavones, mineral salts (especially potassium) and tannins.
Efficacy	Haemostypticum, uterotonicum, diureticum.
Use	Its beneficial effect on haemorrhages has been pharmocologically and clinically proved, but is limited in time (after three months it loses its efficacy). Lowers the blood pressure, acts on the smooth muscle of the uterus, increasing tension. Popularly used for infections of the urinary tract and kidney sand.
Dosage	Usually an infusion (3 teasoonfuls of the drug to a glass of water); drink ⅓-½ glass, 2-3 times a day in cases of excessive menstrual discharge (menorrhagia), slight haemorrhages in the alimentary tract and elsewhere, e.g. nose bleeding.
Warning	In larger doses the drug is toxic: consult a doctor before using.

CENTAURY

Centaurium minus (C. umbellatum)
Gentianaceae
Herba Centaurii — herbage

10-50cm (4-20in) — * — †
Flowers: July-October

Botanical description	Herb with a quadrilateral, errect stem, the upper half branching. Basal leaves form a rosette; on the stem the leaves are opposite, amplexicaul, oval to lanceolate and pointed. Pink sessile flowers (in rare cases white) in subumbellate clusters.
Habitat	Grows almost throughout the whole of Europe from lowland to mountain elevations.
Collection	The young, flowering herbage is collected and the leaves from the basal rosettes are added.
Drying	Dry in thin layers well spread out or in small bunches in the shade (artificial heat up to 40°-45°C) (104°-113°F).
Cultivation	Likes warm, sunny sites, calcareous soil rich in nutriments and nitrogen. The seeds are first sown in boxes or hotbeds, and planted out in spring.
Active constituents	The therapeutically active principles are bitter glycosides, silica and flavones.
Efficacy	Amarum, stomachicum, tonicum.
Use	The drug belongs to the group known as pure bitter principles *(Amara pura)*, which are effective in cases of insufficient gastric secretions, poor digestion in children and elderly people, and loss of appetite. It also helps for atony of the intestines. In popular medicine it is further used as an anthelmintic and hypotensive, and to increase the flow of bile; however, the effects are very weak, even questionable.
Dosage	Decoction: half a teaspoonful of the herbage to ½-1 glass of water; take 1-2 teaspoonfuls 2-4 times a day at least half an hour before meals. You can add 2-8g of the powdered drug to 100ml water to the decoction before drinking. The tincture, which can be bought at a pharmacy, is to be recommended, the dose being approximately 1g taken 30 minutes before meals. The drug is a constituent of gastric herbal teas.

GREATER CELANDINE

+ *Chelidonium majus*
Papaveraceae
+ *Herba Chelidonii* — herbage

30-100cm (12-40in) — ‡
Flowers: April-October
Poisonous Plant

Botanical description	Branching stem, alternate pinnate leaves with oval irregularly lobed leaflets. Flowers in sparse umbels. When broken off the stem secretes an orange-coloured caustic latex.
Habitat	A plant commonly found near human settlements throughout the whole of Europe, and widely naturalized in eastern North America.
Collection	The flowering aerial parts are collected. Wear gloves — the juice has a caustic effect (keep it away from the eyes!).
Drying	Dry in thin layers in well-aired places; keep separate from other plants. If dried by artificial heat, first quickly at 80°C (175°F) and then not more than 35°C (95°F). The drug easily becomes damp and turns mouldy.
Cultivation	Reproduced by seed or vegetatively, the leaf buds taking root. Prefers damp soil with sufficient nitrogen.
Active constituents	The therapeutically active principles are alkaloids, flavones, amines (e.g. histamin) and saponins.
Efficacy	Spasmolyticum, cholagogum, sedativum, bacteriostaticum.
Use	The chelidonic acid prevents cellular division (it has certain cytostatic effects), but it is too toxic. From time to time the drug and its extracts return to therapy and research. The plant is often prepared fresh (drying leads to a certain loss of efficacy). The fresh juice is used in popular medicine to remove warts. Chelidonic acid is extracted from the plant and used as a constituent in pharmaceutical preparations (to relax spasms and increase the flow of bile, for example).
Dosage	Infusion of half a teaspoonful of the drug to a cup of water, one cup to be taken twice a day. Popular medicine recommends it also for an irritative cough, asthma, for relaxing gastric spasms, and easing pain caused by gall bladder disorders.

CHICORY

Cichorium intybus
Cichoriaceae (Asteraceae; Compositae)
Radix Cichorii — root

30-130cm (12-50in) — ‡
Flowers: July-September

Botanical description	Common herb with a fusiform root; the leaves of the basal rosette are pinnatilobate, those on the branching stem entire and lanceolate, reduced to bracts in the inflorescence. The large, pretty light-blue flowers (white only rarely) are clustered in the axils.
Habitat	Widespread species in dry positions; likes nitrogenous soils. Grows at lowland to mountain elevations throughout Europe, and is now widespread in North America.
Collection	The roots of wild Chicory are dug up with a spade in autumn. After cleaning they are quickly washed and left to drip dry.
Drying	Roots are usually cut into pieces about 15cm (6in) long and dried quickly, in a shady place. For best results, dry by artificial heat (40°-50°C; 104°-122°F).
Cultivation	For pharmaceutical purposes the plants used are exclusively those growing in the wild. The cultivated varieties are used in the food industry for the production of coffee substitutes and additives.
Active constituents	The root contains chiefly bitter principles tied to glycosides, tannins, choline, arginine and inulin, reserve polysaccharide.
Efficacy	Cholagogum, diureticum, stomachicum, tonicum, metabolicum; inulinum: dieteticum.
Use	The bitter principles encourage the secretion of bile and are beneficial to the stomach (cultivated roots do not contain them, which is why they are unacceptable) and the drug is therefore a component of herbal teas on account of its inulin content. Equal parts of Chicory and Dandelion root (one tablespoonful to a cup of water, boiled 5 minutes) is a mixture recommended to increase the flow of bile, but it is not fully reliable.
Dosage	5g for a cup of infusion, or boil briefly. Drink ½ glass 2-4 times a day.

MEADOW SAFFRON, AUTUMN CROCUS

5-20cm (2-8in) — ‡

+ *Colchicum autumnale*
Liliaceae
+ *Semen Colchici* — seed

Flowers: August-October
Poisonous Plant
•

Botanical description	Pear-shaped scaly corm, from which pink or pinkish-purple flowers grow in autumn. After pollination, and in spring the following year, there appears a perianth on a short stem with a split capsule containing a great quantity of blackish-brown seeds, together with a rosette of elongated lanceolate leaves.
Habitat	Frequently found in damp meadows from lowland to mountain elevations throughout Europe.
Collection	The ripe capsules are cut off and the seeds shaken out.
Drying	The capsules are first left to dry thoroughly, and when the seeds have been shaken out they are further dried in the sun.
Cultivation	The meadow saffron likes deep, loamy, well-nourished damp soil, rich in nitrogen. In some countries the subterranean part is protected.
Active constituents	The whole plant — but the seeds in particular — contains poisonous alkaloids, above all colchicine, the so-called plant arsenic. The others are not of interest and are not used.
Efficacy	Antiarthriticum, antimitoticum, antiuraticum.
Use	Pure colchicine and all preparations containing it must be prescribed by a qualified physician. It is generally prescribed as an antiuraticum for acute gout (it has no influence on other forms of arthritis). It can be used to relieve pain (antidolorozum). Colchine is very effective in relieving acute attacks of gout, decreasing the inflammatory reaction while not increasing the secretion of urinal acid. The connection between the antiuratic and antimitotic effects which colchine has is not yet clear. Colchine is also a cellular poison — it inhibits cell division (mitosis). In cultivars it increases the number of chromosomes in the plants and thus assists the growth of their green parts.
Warning	Use only under medical supervision.

LILY-OF-THE-VALLEY

+ *Convallaria majalis*
Liliaceae
Herba Convallariae — herbage; *Folia Convallariae* — leaf

15-25cm (6-10in) — ‡
Flowers: May-June
Poisonous Plant

Botanical description	The herb has a thin rhizome from which there firstly grow two elliptic pointed leaves, then from their centre a scape bearing a unilateral raceme of pretty, scented flowers. The fruits are round, red berries.
Habitat	Grows almost throughout Europe, abundant in thin, deciduous woodland as well as in subalpine coniferous forests; the Lily-of-the-Valley found in the Allegheny Mountains is probably *C. montana*, a related species.
Collection	The flowering aerial parts are collected, or, more frequently, just the leaf.
Drying	Can be dried in bunches, but better results are achieved with thin layers in a very well-aired spot. The drug is usually of better quality when dried by artificial heat at 40°-60°C; (104°-140°F).
Cultivation	Prefers warm, shady spots, fairly damp soil rich in minerals. Usually reproduced vegetatively — by cuttings of the rhizomes with buds.
Active constituents	Mainly cardenoloid glucosides (about 17), which have a steroid basis. Flavones, saponins and chelidonic acid are also present.
Efficacy	Cardiotonicum, diureticum.
Use	For therapeutic use the leaf is titrated, and then it forms a basic element in pharmaceutical preparations, sometimes also in herbal teas *(Species cardiaceae)*. More frequently it is used in tinctures and extracts, which are further combined in medicines used as cardiotonics or as diuretics.
Dosage	Infusions of the leaves are now out of date and rarely prescribed; occasionally a standardized dose of powdered leaf is administered. More frequently the tincture is prescribed (dosage: 0.5g taken once, 2.5g for the whole day). Preparations are prescribed by a doctor.
Warning	Lily-of-the-Valley is a toxic plant which is often the cause of poisoning, the danger being underestimated.

CORIANDER

Coriandrum sativum
Daucaceae (Umbelliferae)
Fructus Coriandri — fruit

30-50cm (12-20in) — *
Flowers: June-July

Botanical description	Round, hairless, striate stem. Lower leaves petiolate, pinnate with ovate lobes; upper leaves bipinnate, amplexicaul, 2-3 times pinnately divided. Tiny flowers in small compound umbels. Fruit orbicular.
Habitat	Originating in the Mediterranean region, it is grown almost everywhere in Europe; wild coriander in North America is an escapee from cultivation.
Collection	The collection of the fruit begins when at least ⅓ of the fruits in the umbels are ripe (yellowish-brown). The whole herb is gathered and tied up in small bundles.
Drying	The bundles are dried in the usual way. After threshing the fruits are further dried at temperatures up to 35°-40°C (95°-104°F).
Cultivation	Needs calcareous soil, but ground can be of poorer quality. Sunny positions, sheltered from the wind. The seeds are sown out in the field in spring; they germinate within two weeks and need moisture.
Active constituents	The whole plant, but the fruit in particular, contains silica (chief elements: linalool and coumarins), tannins, vitamin C, phytoncides, proteins and volatile oil.
Efficacy	Carminativum, spasmolyticum, corrigens, stomachicum, nervinum.
Use	The fruits are now used more as a medicament than as a spice. They have a marked carminative effect (for flatulence); they increase the secretion of gastric juices; have a beneficial effect in non-specific digestive disorders and colics. Usually combined with other drugs, only rarely used alone.
Dosage	The infusion is made of 2-3g of the crushed fruits to a glass of water; drink 2-3 cups a day. The silica, with its relatively high content of linalool, can be used to improve aroma and taste in the pharmaceutical and food industries. The fruit provides one of the basic components in curry powder. Silica is also used in ointments for rheumatism and as a nervine.

WOOD HAWTHORN, MIDLAND HAWTHORN

1.5-8m (5-25ft) — * * — ‡‡

Crataegus laevigata (C. oxyacantha, C. oxycanthoides)
Rosaceae   **Flowers: May-June**
Flores Crataegi — flower; *Folia Crataegi* — leaf; *Fructus Crataegi* — fruit

Botanical description	Small, thickly branching, thorny tree. Laterally oval leaf with 3-5 lobes broader than long, edges irregularly dentate. Scented flowers in corymbs. Fruits ovoid berries, red and astringent when mature.
Habitat	Grows at the edge of woods, in thickets and on wasteland throughout the whole of Europe. Often found in hedges and gardens. Many related species grow in North America (see warning at end).
Collection	Collection made only from specimens with white flowers. The flower is picked with a short stalk at the beginning of the flowering period, as is the leaf. The fruit must be ripe, without peduncles.
Drying	Dry quickly, artificial heat up to 35°C (95°F). The fruit is left to dry in thin layers, in a well-ventilated spot, then the drying process is completed at temperatures up to 70°C (155°F).
Cultivation	Prefers loamy, dampish, calcareous soils and a shady position. No special care required.
Active constituents	Flavones, triterpencarbonic acids, amino acids, tannins; the fruit also contains sugars and colouring as well as vitaminds C and B.
Efficacy	Spasmolyticum, cardiacum, angiotonicum, diureticum.
Use	Drugs and preparations containing Hawthorn increase and regulate the flow of blood through the coronary arteries, improve and strengthen the action of the heart, vascular tone, and therefore serve to improve the action of the weak and ageing heart. Hawthorn regulates the blood circulation, especially in cases of high blood pressure, exhaustion, tiredness, inflammation of the heart muscle, general weakness in old age. It is used for menopausal disorders, spasms and as a diuretic.
Dosage	An infusion of 2 teaspoonfuls to one cup is usually drunk 2-3 times a day. Tinctures and extracts are more frequently used.
Warning	The applications of a similar European species, Common Hawthorn *(Crataegus monogyna)* are the same. Cultivated species, as well as those with full or coloured flowers, are *not* collected and used.

FOXGLOVE

+ *Digitalis purpurea*
Scrophulariaceae
Folia Digitalis purpureae — leaf

30-150cm (1-5ft) — †
Flowers: June-August
Poisonous Plant

Botanical description	A striking, pretty herb with whitish hairs; erect stem, alternate dentate leaves ovate and tapering. The flowers have bell-shaped corollas arranged in a thick drooping cluster on one side.
Habitat	Scattered through thin woods from foothill to mountain elevations. Protected everywhere.
Collection	The leaf is collected from cultivated plants in their fifth or sixth months.
Drying	Dried only by artificial heat, not over 62°C (144°F).
Cultivation	Very sensitive to soil and climate; grows in light soil free of weeds, well supplied with ground-water, humus and nutrients. Warm, sunny, sheltered sites. The tiny seeds are sown out on the surface of flattened soil (they germinate in the light) and are pressed down with a board. Sowing can be done in spring; as a winter crop until the end of February. Seedlings are planted out in a grid pattern 40cm (15in) apart when the leaves are about 10cm (4in) long. Herbicides are not used, the Foxglove being very sensitive to them.
Active constituents	Mainly digitaloids — cardenolides, purpurea-glycosides. Flavones, steroidal saporins, anthraquinones and mucilages.
Efficacy	Cardiotonicum, diureticum.
Use	For medical use as a cardiotonicum the leaf is titrated. It can then be used in the preparation of a variety of medicaments which serve mainly to strengthen contractions in cardiac insufficiency.
Dosage	Infusion (1.25g of the leaf to 190ml of water, one teaspoonful 3 times a day) is a rare form; more often used as a tincture (40-50 drops 3 times a day for 3 days, then 5-15 drops), or isolated substances used.
Warning	Therapy can be undertaken and prescribed only by a qualified doctor. Certain other varieties of the Foxglove family are also used therapeutically.

COMMON HORSE-TAIL

Equisetum arvense
Equisetaceae
Herba Equiseti — herbage

10-60cm (4-24in) — ‡
Dilation of the spores: in spring

Botanical description	Spring herb, not branching, fertile stems terminating in a brown spike of sporiferous leaves. After these have disappeared, sterile pale-green stems develop bearing verticil branches.
Habitat	A weed growing in damp meadows and fields and by the wayside.
Collection	Only the green, summer (sterile) stems are collected.
Drying	Dry quickly in thin layers. Artificial heat up to 40°C (105°F) maximum.
Cultivation	Reproduced from the tiny, green spores growing in the sporangia on the spring stems. No need for cultivation — grows abundantly in the wild.
Active constituents	Mineral salts — silicates and potassium nitrate — flavones and a few saponins, organic acids.
Efficacy	Diureticum, haemostaticum, antiscleroticum, desinficiens.
Use	The soluble silicates support certain therapeutic processes (lung diseases; they reduced the rupture of blood capilliaries as well as the formation of stones, stop minor internal haemorrhages, help to rid the body of harmful substances, known as remineralization, and are said to increase the resistivity of the white blood cells.).
Dosage	Decoction of 10-20g of the drug to 2 glasses of water, boil 15 minutes. Drink half a glass 3-4 times a day. The drug is not usually used therapeutically by itself. It is a component of diuretic herbal teas as well as those used in the treatment of rheumatism, arthritis, and heart and lung disorders. Used as a gargle and for baths, boil 100g herbage for 20 minutes for rheumatism, neuralgia, perspiring feet, local disorders of the blood circulation. Popular medicine uses it internally for coughs, hoarseness, bronchitis and externally for eczemas, badly healing wounds, haematomas, and for sitz-baths for kidney diseases (in combination with internal treatment).
Warning	Related species are toxic.

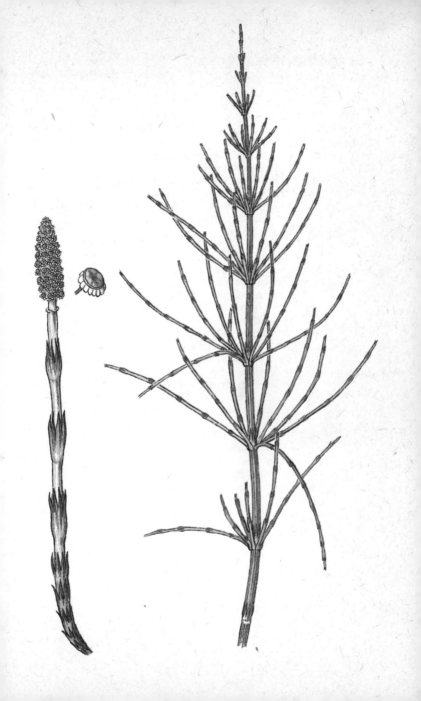

LARGE-FLOWERED STICKY EYEBRIGHT 5-25cm (2-20in)— *

Euphrasia rostkoviana (E. officinalis)
Scrophulariaceae
Herba Euphrasiae — herbage

Flowers: July-October

Botanical description	Small bushy herb; slender ascending stems, thickly leaved. Opposite, almost amplexicaul oval leaves, obtusely dentate. Large, symmetrical, two-lipped flowers in terminal whorls.
Habitat	At the edge of forests, on meadows and pastures.
Collection	The herbage is collected in the flowering period.
Drying	Dry in the shade in thin layers or in small bundles. Where artificial heat is used, up to 40°C (104°F).
Cultivation	Semi-parasitic plant. Grows well in semi-dry, non-calcareous soils. Cultivation out of the question — very abundant in the wild.
Active constituents	Rich in glycocides. Also contains tannins, bitter substances, mineral salts (mainly magnesia and copper), silica with coumarins and polyphenolic substances.
Efficacy	Antiphlogisticum, adstringens, antiasthmaticum, stomachicum.
Use	Well-known and popular home remedy for inflammation of the eyes (eye-baths, compresses), usually in combination with Chamomile flowers, Fennel and boric acid. Used for respiratory disorders, as a weak stomachic, metabolic, to lower blood pressure in combination with Mistletoe herbage, Garlic and other drugs). Popularly used for severe headaches and mild insomnia.
Dosage	For eye-baths and compresses: 5 per cent infusion (cover and leave to stand 25 minutes). Otherwise usual dose: 2-3g powdered drug 3 times a day. Believed to increase the flow of gastric juices. Also 2 per cent infusion, or 3 teaspoonfuls of the drug to 2 glasses of water; drink 2 glasses a day.
Warning	Do not increase internal doses unnecessarily. The herb is very polymorphic — a mixture of related species can be collected.

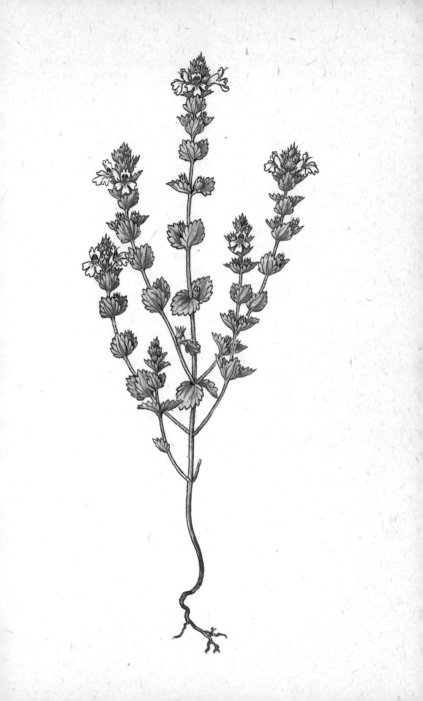

FENNEL

Foeniculum vulgare
Daucaceae (Umbelliferae)
Fructus Foeniculi — fruit;

80-200cm (2½-6½ft) — ‡
Flowers: July-August

Botanical description	Stem erect, branching, striate, glaucous; leaf segments long, capillary. Flowers in compound umbels. Fruit oval, brownish, aromatic carpophores.
Habitat	Indigenous in the Mediterranean region of western Asia, it is now grown worldwide.
Collection	Collection begins when at least one-third of the fruits in the umbels are ripe. The umbels are cut off, dried and threshed. The drug is of better quality if the fruits are collected in stages as they ripen (combed fennel).
Drying	The fruits are dried at a maximum temperature of 35°-40°C (95°-104°F).
Cultivation	Prefers fertile, damp, calcareous soil and sunny positions sheltered from the wind. Sow thickly in beds in spring, and protect the plants from frost in the winter. In the spring of the second year they can be planted out.
Active constituents	Chiefly silica containing anethole and fenchyl. The fruit also has oil, sugars, organic acids and proteins.
Efficacy	Expectorans, carminativum, amaro-tonicum, lactogogum, corrigens.
Use	As an expectorant it is combined with Licorice root and Peppermint leaf; for digestive disorders and flatulence it is combined with Caraway, Coriander, Aniseed. Often prescribed by itself for children and babies; improves the appetite, helps in cases of chronic constipation, relaxes spasms.
Dosage	For babies as a carminative: a pinch to ½ teaspoonful for a glass of infusion, administered by the teaspoonful. The usual dosage: 0.3-0.8g for an infusion, 2-3 times a day as a stomachic or carminative. Adults can take up to a tablespoonful of the seeds to 2 glasses of infusion and drink ⅓-½ a glass 2-3 times a day as an expectorant (older children one teaspoonful every 3 hours). The drug is also recommended for nursing mothers, and it improves the circulation in the pelvic region (assists menstruation).

WILD STRAWBERRY

8-25cm (3-25in) — ↕

Fragaria vesca

Flowers: May-June

Rosaceae

Folia Fragariae — leaf; *Fructus Fragariae* — fruit

Botanical description	Well-known plant with fairly large trifoliate leaves and numerous stolons. The flowers ripen into red strawberries.
Habitat	Species spread worldwide, frequent from lowland to subalpine elevations, especially in forest clearings and at the edge of woods.
Collection	Only collect the young leaves of wild plants; fruits when mature. Collect in firm containers, preferably baskets to keep the lower layers well-aired.
Drying	The leaves with short peduncles are dried in thin layers, in well-ventilated places. Artificial heat must not exceed 50°C (122°F). The fruit is usually used fresh, but can be dried (requires experience and artificial heat, e.g. in the oven — take care not to burn.
Cultivation	Cultivated species are not used in pharmacy.
Active constituents	Leaf: mainly tannins, mineral salts, flavones, vitamin C and small quantities of silica. Fruit: sugars, pectin, acids and aromatic substances.
Efficacy	Adstringens, diureticum, metabolicum.
Use	The leaf is very popular as a home remedy; it does not have a clearly defined physiological effect.
Dosage	Decoctions and infusions are drunk (about 5-20g of the leaf to 2 glasses of water) ½ glass 3-4 times a day. The drug is rarely used alone, usually combined. A frequent component of so-called 'daily' teas. The fruits are a nutritious and healthy delicacy, an important fruit of the forest, suited for use at home and in the food industry. Added for their flavour to jams made from cultivated and garden strawberries. For home use the leaves are sometimes fermented, which increases their aroma and gives the tea a richer colour.
Warning	Sensitive people are often allergic to the fruit.

COMMON FUMITORY

(+) *Fumaria officinalis*
Papaveraceae (Fumariaceae)
(+) *Herba Fumariae* — herbage

15-30cm (6-12in) — *
Flowers: May-October
Poisonous Plant

Botanical description	Frail herb with a hollow, angular, branching stem. Petiolated tripinnate leaves; small flowers in loose racemes.
Habitat	Frequent on wasteland throughout Europe and in fields from lowland to mountain elevations. Garden weed.
Collection	Cut the herbage off above ground or pull up the whole plant and cut off the root.
Drying	Dry in thin layers — extremely fragile, turn with care! Artificial heat to 35°C (95°F) — some authors say up to 50°C (122°F). Mildly toxic.
Cultivation	The seeds are sown thinly or scattered over garden beds.
Active constituents	Chiefly alkaloids, some of which are known, but the majority are tied to fumaric acid. Bitter principles, tannins and mineral salts (potassium) are also present.
Efficacy	Cholereticum, diureticum, stomachicum, metabolicum.
Use	The alkaloids act mainly on the smooth muscle of the gall bladder and stimulate the secretion of bile. Their diuretic and laxative effect is fairly weak, they are used more as depuratives and metabolics. They are considered as adjuvants in the dissolution of gall stones, they relieve spasms in facial migraine; externally, they are applied to haematomas.
Dosage	The infusion is usually used (2-3 teaspoonfuls to 2 glasses of water — macerate 3-4 hours); a teaspoonful of the infusion 3-5 times a day. The drug is not usually used by itself, but is combined with other similarly effective drugs (as a spasmolytic, with Peppermint, Fennel and so on). It is also popularly used as a skin cleansing agent.
Warning	Larger doses of the drug impair respiration (the daily dose of 2 teaspoonfuls to 2 glasses of water should not be exceeded — only on the advice of a doctor).

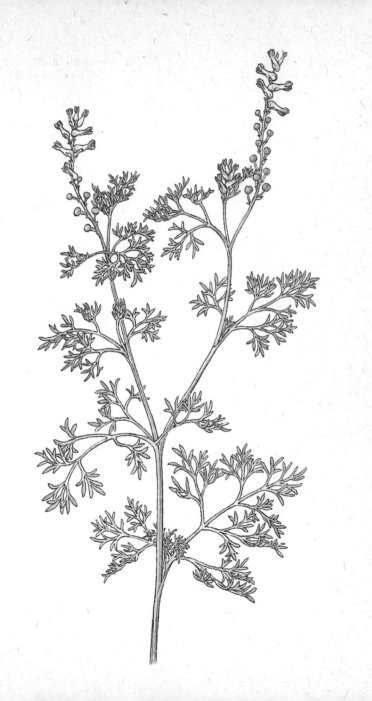

GOAT'S RUE

(+) *Galega officinalis*
Viciaceae (Fabaceae; Papilionaceae)
Herba Galegae — herbage; *Semen Galegae* - seed

40-80cm (15-30in) — ‡
Flowers: July-August
Caution

Botanical description	Glabrous herb, stem usually simple, erect, striate and hollow. Unevenly pinnate leaves on short petioles, 5-9 pairs of oblong and lanceolate leaves. Oblong clusters of numerous purplish-blue, sometimes white, flowers on long peduncles.
Habitat	Mediterranean, continental European species — grows in damp, marshy meadows, on river banks.
Collection	Herbage in the flowering period. The seeds are shaken out after the fruit has ripened.
Drying	Dry in shady, well-ventilated places; if by artificial heat, not over 60°C (140°F). The seeds are dried in the usual way.
Cultivation	Requires fresh, loamy soil, rich in humus and nutrients, with ground-water. Warm, sheltered position. The seed is usually sown in spring (up to the beginning of May); appears within a week.
Active constituents	Chiefly galagine and peganine, also other basic substances — then tannins, saporins, bitter principles, sugar, flavones and oil.
Efficacy	Antidiabeticum, diureticum, diaphoreticum, galactagogum.
Use	Galagine lowers the sugar content in the blood, but it is quite toxic; it cannot replace insulin! Combine with Bilberry leaf, pericarp of ripe Beans, Dandelion root, Sage and Stinging Nettle leaves. An infusion is made of the herbage: 4 teaspoonfuls to 2 glasses of water, bring to the boil, leave to stand 30 minutes and drink ⅓-½ glass 3 times a day. The dosage and usage of the seeds is similar. Extracts from Goat's Rue are mixed in ointments (1.5 per cent) and applied to skin wounds; they also increase the effects of X-rays and heal skin defects. It is questionable whether this drug increases lactation; official medicine does not use it for this purpose. Apart from that, its value as fodder is doubtful.
Warning	Larger doses cause poisoning.

DOWNY HEMP-NETTLE

Galeopsis segetum
Lamiaceae (Labiatae)
Herba Galeopsidis — herbage

10-40cm (4-15in) — *
Flowers: July-August

Botanical description	Branching stem; opposite petiolate leaves, ovally lanceolate, widely dentate at the edges. The stem terminates in 4-8 whorls of calceolate flowers.
Habitat	Usually grows in fields among cereals and on wasteland. Indigenous to western Europe. There are many similar species, but there is no need to distinguish between them — it can be assumed they have the same active principles.
Collection	The flowering herbage from this and other species — above all from the Common Hemp-nettle *(Galeopsis tetrahit)*, which has pink flowers and is a very abundant weed in fields or by the roadside. The stems should not be thicker than 5mm ($^1/_5$in) on average.
Drying	Dry in a current of air, in thin, well-spread layers. Artificial heat (maximum 35°-40°C; 95°-104°F) is recommended to finish off the drying process.
Cultivation	Likes dry, sandy, somewhat calcareous soil and warmth. The seeds are sown in autumn or early in spring.
Active constituents	Hemp-nettles have more or less the same active principles: tannins, silicic acid (part so-called soluble), saponins, bitter principles, silica and pectins.
Efficacy	Expectorans, diureticum, stomachicum, adstringens.
Use	This drug has similar properties to Horse-tail, which is why it has long been used for bronchitis, at one time also for tuberculosis, and for asthma. It is a good expectorant and mild astringent. Rarely used by itself.
Dosage	Infusion: 15-25g of the drug to 2 glasses of water; half a glass 3 times a day. The usual combination is the well-known Kobert silicate mixture: equal parts of Hemp-nettle, Horse-tail and Common Knotgrass; 2 teaspoonfuls of the tea to a glass of water. As an expectorant it is mixed with Coltsfoot, Ribwort Plantain and Lungwort leaves. To help the excretion of mineral substances in the organism it is combined with the herbage of Common Knotgrass, Horse-tail and Lungwort.

GREAT YELLOW GENTIAN

40-140cm (15-55in) — ‡
Gentiana lutea
Gentianaceae
Radix Gentianae — root

Flowers: June-August

Botanical description	Plant with a long, thick root and simple, erect, hollow stem. Clusters of yellow peduncled flowers in the axils of opposite, elliptic leaves.
Habitat	In the mountainous regions of Europe and Asia Minor; protected everywhere except in the Balkans.
Collection	The roots are dug up in autumn after the end of the flowering period.
Drying	Best dried rapidly by artificial heat (45°-60°C; 113°-140°F). The fermentation of the root for pharmaceutical purposes is not allowed.
Cultivation	Prefers deep, calcareous soils, damp from time to time, and shady positions. Usually propagated by the seed, sown in autumn for the cultivation of seedlings. Planted out in the autumn of the second year. Can be harvested in the 6th-7th years. Flowers in about the 10th-15th years.
Active constituents	Bitter principles tied to glycosides. the drug is one of those with pure bitter principles (amara pura).
Efficacy	Amarum, stomachicum, tonicum, cholagogum.
Use	Chiefly for loss of appetite, dyspepsia, chronic gastric catarrh, and in particular for insufficient gastric juices. Also used for intestinal disorders.
Dosage	The root is used in powder form, 0.5 to 1g, 2-3 times a day, or as a decoction (5g of the drug to 200ml water, boil 5 minutes), drink a teaspoonful 30 minutes before meals. The tincture is the most useful form: take 30 drops in a glass or water 2-5 times a day after meals.
Note	Drugs with bitter principles (amara pura) should be administered together with silicic acids to increase their effect.

HERB BENNET, WOOD AVENS

(+) *Geum urbanum*
Rosaceae
(+) *Radix (Rhizoma) Caryophyllatae* — root (rhizome)

25-50cm (10-20in) — ‡
Flowers: June-October
Caution

Botanical description	Fleshy rhizome; basal rosette; angular, sparsely branching, hairy stems terminating in a single flower. The leaves on the stem are pinnate with three unevenly dentate leaflets, large stipules.
Habitat	Widespread in the temperate regions of Europe, from lowland to mountain elevations. Grows on waste ground, in damp sparse woodland, by the wayside, in thickets; often to be found among nitrate-loving plants.
Collection	The underground parts are dug up in autumn.
Drying	Clean or briefly wash and leave to drip, then dry rapidly. Artificial heat not over 35°-40°C (95°-104°F). The drug easily becomes damp.
Cultivation	Herb Bennet likes very damp, nitrogenous soils. Propagate by seed or division of the roots.
Active constituents	Chiefly mildly toxic silica (with eugenol — similar to that in cloves), then tannins, bitter principles, flavones, sugars and enzymes.
Efficacy	Stomachicum, adstringens, antidiarrhoicum, desinficiens.
Use	Used almost exclusively in home remedies. The aromatic rhizome has long been used as a spice and it is usually added to wines and liqueurs; it can be used in cooking instead of cinnamon and cloves. It stimulates the stomach, calms the nerves and acts as an expectorant.
Dosage	Either in powder form (2-5g) or as an infusion (5 per cent); leave to stand 15 minutes and drink 2-4 cups a day. In southern Europe the drug is macerated in wine (25-80g daily dose of wine). It is believed to reduce excessive acidity of the stomach, lower fevers and cure chronic diarrhoea. Used externally for gargles in cases of inflammation of the throat or mouth. Eliminates unpleasant mouth odour. A related species, Water Avens *(Geum rivale)*, found throughout the North Temperate Zone, has similar efficacy.

98

GROUND IVY, FIELD BALM

(+) *Glechoma hederacea*
Lamiaceae (Labiatae)
Herba Glechomae — herbage

15-60cm (6-24in) — ‡
Flowers: March-May
Poisonous Plant

Botanical description	Shortish, ascending stems with creeping shoots up to 50cm (20in) long. Opposite, petiolate, reniform leaves with crenate edges. Flowers on short peduncles in the axils, blue-purple, sometimes white in colour.
Habitat	Eurasian species; grows as a weed among field crops, on the edge of deciduous and coniferous woods and in woodland clearings.
Collection	The flowering top parts or the leafy stems are collected.
Drying	Dried at a temperature of 35°-40°C (95°-104°F). Dries quickly.
Cultivation	Ground Ivy likes fresh, damp, loamy soils, containing nutrients and nitrogen.
Active constituents	Mainly tannins, a bitter principle, silica, choline, organic acids and a considerable quantity of mineral salts. The bitter principle is toxic for horses.
Efficacy	Adstringens, depurativum, stomachicum, expectorans, diureticum, antiphlogisticum.
Use	Stimulates the secretion of gastric juices, assists digestion; it has long been used as a home remedy for respiratory troubles. An antidiarrhoetic and anti-inflammatory agent on account of its high tannin content. It helps to eliminate harmful substances in the blood and to dissolve gall stones.
Dosage	Usual dose: 1½ teaspoonfuls of the drug for an infusion in 2 glasses of water; drink half a glass 2-3 times a day. For external use, a decoction of 15-25g of the drug, boiled about 3 minutes, in 2 glasses of water; the decoction is suitable for baths and compresses.

On account of its pleasant aroma and spicy flavour the leaves are used as a culinary spice — especially for soups, omelettes, cheeses and butter — in a similar way to parsley. It is also used early in spring as an ingredient in spring salads.

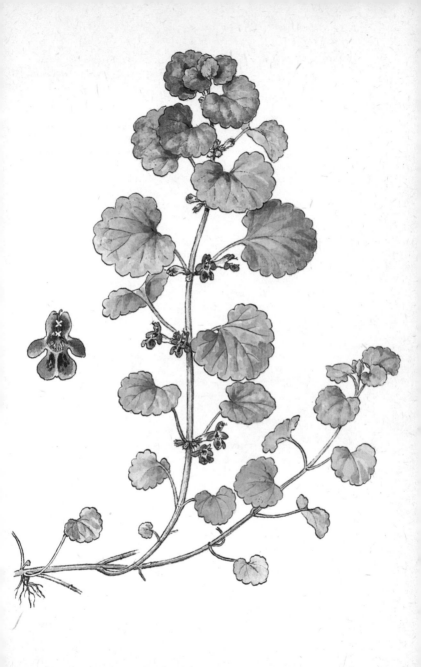

LICORICE (LIQUORICE)

Glycyrrhiza glabra
Viciaceae (Fabaceae; Papilionaceae)
Radix Liquiritieae (Radix Glycyrrhizae) — root

15-150cm (1½-5ft) — ‡
Flowers: June, sometimes July

Botanical description	Branching stems; pinnate leaves with an odd number of lanceolate leaflets, somewhat hairy on the underside. Numerous flowers in clusters on axillary peduncles. Fruits: oblong pods.
Habitat	Species indigenous to southern Europe and Asia Minor. Fairly frequently cultivated in the past.
Collection	The roots and stolons are dug up in the autumn of the third year of vegetation, and are sometimes stripped of the bark.
Drying	Best results are achieved with artificial heat at temperatures between 20° and 35°C (68°-95°F).
Cultivation	Requires a dry climate, a warm, sunny, sheltered position; deep, permeable soil rich in nutrients. The seeds are sown in rows to produce seedlings which are planted out in April or September. Can also be propagated vegetatively.
Active constituents	Saponins, flavones, bitter substances, resins, silica, organic acids and triterpenes.
Efficacy	Expectorans, spasmolyticum, antiphlogisticum, diureticum, corrigens.
Use	The drug has an expectorant effect which increases the secretion of the bronchial glands. A mild diuretic and laxative. Research has proved its long-known effect on stomach ulcers. Rarely used alone. It is a common component of many herbal teas, diuretic, laxative, expectorant and teas for flatulence; extracts are added to many galenical preparations or industrially-produced medicaments for summer diarrhoea, diseases of the urinary tract, gastric troubles. It is used as flavouring in the confectionary, food and liqueur industries.
Dosage	The usual dose for a decoction or infusion of the root is 1.5g (usually 2-3g or more a day). A thickened water extract *(Succus liquiritiae)* is often used as a home remedy or in the food industry.
Warning	The drug is not toxic, but it should not be used over a long period of time and the dosage should not be increased unnecessarily.

SMOOTH RUPTURE WORT

Herniaria glabra
Silenaceae (Caryophyllaceae)
Herba Herniariae — herbage

5-20cm (2-8in) — ‡
Flowers: June-October

Botanical description	Branching, glabrous herb. The spreading, recumbent stems usually form roundish clumps. Minute flowers in tight clusters. Leaves small, alternate, oblong.
Habitat	A common European weed found on wasteland, rubbish dumps, by the roadside, from lowland to mountain elevations.
Collection	The aerial parts are collected during the flowering season. Sometimes it is possible to collect a second time in the autumn.
Drying	Clean thoroughly (can be quickly washed and left to drip), dry quickly in temperatures up to 35°-40°C (95°-104°F).
Cultivation	Prefers nitrogenous, but not calcareous soils; sow in sandy soil on sunny slopes.
Active constituents	The important substances are saponins, coumarins, flavones and silica; organic acids and anthocyans are also present.
Efficacy	Diureticum, spasmolyticum, urodesinficiens, bacteriostaticum.
Use	The drug acts as a spasmolyticum, especially in the urinary tract, facilitates the flow of urine, increases the excretion of salts, dissolves stones in the urinary bladder and in the urethra (the addition of soda bicarbonate to the infusion is sometimes recommended).
Dosage	The usual dosage for an infusion of the drug is about one teaspoonful to a glass of water; drink 2-4 times a day between meals. Not used alone: it is a constituent chiefly of diuretic and urological herbal teas, as well as those administered for gall and kidney stones, for inflammations, spasms and menstruation troubles.
Note	A related species, *Herniaria hirsuta* (Hairy Rupture Wort) is similarly effective. Fairly rare, it grows in warm sandy and grassy spots; when dried it smells like coumarin.

HOP

2-8m (6-26ft) — ‡
Flowers: July-August

Humulus lupulus
Cannabaceae
Strobilus Lupuli — strobiles; *Glandulae lupuli*; *Lupulinum* — lupulin

Botanical description	Dioecious liana with climbing stems 6-8m (20-26ft) long, with hooked hairs. Opposite as well as petiolate alternate, palmate, pinnatilobate (3-5 lobes) and cordate leaves with serrate edges. Wild hops or hops that have run wild are of no value for the pharmaceutical and brewing industries.
Habitat	Hops growing wild or as an escape grow almost everywhere in the northern hemisphere, and commonly form thickets in woods.
Collection	The pistillate catkins (strobiles) of cultivated plants are collected in autumn and the grains on the surface of the bracts (lupulin) are shaken out.
Drying	The strobiles are dried in special drying rooms at 40°C-50°C (100°-122°F). The lupulins are obtained by sifting and cleaning the dried ripe male inflorescences, and are then further left to dry.
Cultivation	Needs permeable, calcareous soil, well supplied with humus.
Active constituents	The strobiles contain chiefly silica (0.5-3 per cent), the composition of which varies according to the geographic origin of the plant. The important substances in the lupulins is the resin, containing bitter principles.
Efficacy	Sedativum, stomachicum, antisepticum, anaphrodisiacum.
Use	The active constituents act as sedatives, increase the secretion of the gastric glands, have a bacteriostatic and bactericidal effect, low toxicity; unfortunately they disintegrate quickly and thus lose their efficacy.
Dosage	The usual dosage for an infusion of the strobiles is one teaspoonful to a glass of water; drink ¼- ⅓ glass 2-3 times a day (as a stomachic before meals, otherwise after meals as a sedative or antispasmodic). The dosage for the grains — the lupulins — is 0.25g, 2-4 times a day 30 minutes before meals as a stomachic, after meals as a sedative or nervine.

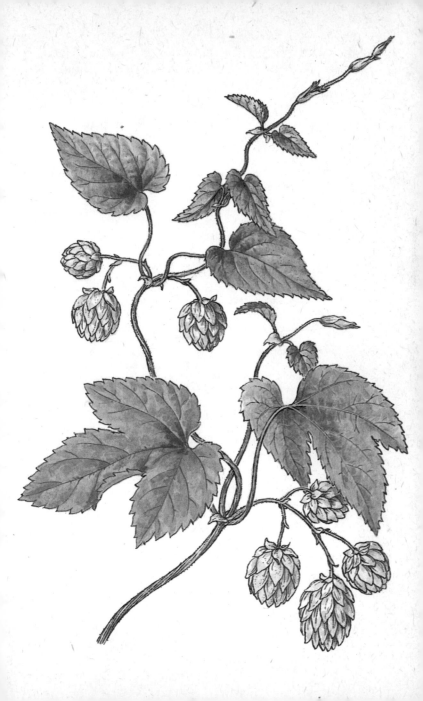

PERFORATE ST. JOHN'S WORT

Hypericum perforatum
Hypericaceae
Herba Hyperici – herbage

30-60cm (1-2ft) — ⚥
Flowers: June-October

Botanical description	Erect glabrous stem. Amplexicaul, elliptic, obtuse leaves with many pellucid dots and tiny black glands along the edge. The numerous peduncled flowers, fairly large, form a wide panicle.
Habitat	Grows throughout the temperate Northern Hemisphere from lowland to mountain elevations. Found in grassland and forest undergrowth.
Collection	The flowering aerial parts are collected without the woody parts of the stalk.
Drying	Dry quickly in thin layers. If not dried thoroughly the drug is easily attacked by mildew.
Cultivation	Prefers semi-dry, fertile calcareous soils and sunny positions. Grows abundantly in the wild — cultivation is therefore unnecessary.
Active constituents	Flavones, silica, tannins, diantrones, red colouring (hypericines) and bacteriostatic resins.
Efficacy	Spasmolyticum, adstringens, stomachicum, diureticum, sedativum; externally: advulnans (for wounds).
Use	A long-known remedy for disorders of the respiratory tracts as well as of the gall-bladder. Is a good anti-inflammatory and disinfectant agent. Effective against bed-wetting in children, disturbed sleep, nervous irritation, depressions, migraine, insufficient secretion of gastric and digestive juices. It has a particularly favourable action on the secretion of the bile, and in cases of stones. Externally it is used on wounds, as a gargle, etc.
Dosage	In general an infusion is prepared of 15-25g of the drug to 2 glasses of water; drink ½ glass 2-3 times a day before meals. After meals it is used as a carminative and in the evening as an antinervine or diuretic.
Warning	The red hypericines cause skin pigmentation problems. During treatment with St. John's Wort avoid exposure to the sun and do not increase the dosage unnecessarily.

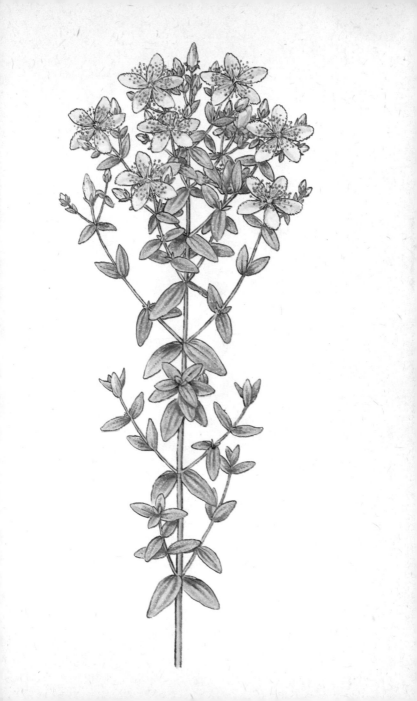

HYSSOP

Hyssopus officinalis
Lamiaceae (Labiatae)
Herba hyssopi — herbage

20-60cm (8-24in) — ††
Flowers: July-October

Botanical description	Semi-shrub; erect and ascending, glabrous stems growing in clumps. Aplexicaul, opposite, narrow leaves, stiff and turned under at the edges. Peduncled blue flowers (sometimes white) growing in clusters in the axils.
Habitat	Indigenous to southern Europe. Has a long history of cultivation. Now naturalized in North America.
Collection	The aerial parts are cut off together with the flowers.
Drying	Care must be taken — the leaves tend to fall off; if artificial heat is used, not over 35°-40°C (95°-104°F).
Cultivation	Prefers sunny positions, light, dryish, calcareous soil. The seeds are sown in the open, or initially in hotbeds. The plant can also be propagated by dividing the roots.
Active constituents	Mainly silica, then tannins, flavones and mineral salts.
Efficacy	Antihydroticum, expectorans, stomachicum, adstringens.
Use	The antihydrotic effect is similar to that of Common Sage. Used as an auxiliary medicine for respiratory disorders; particularly suitable for elderly patients. Encourages the secretion of gastric juices, improves the digestion. External use: as a gargle for inflammations, etc.
Dosage	For external use (compresses): decoction or infusion of a teaspoonful of the drug to a glass of water, or 2g to 1½ glasses. Internally, an infusion of two teaspoonfuls to 2 glasses of water is drunk — ⅓ glass 2-3 times a day, or an infusion of 1½ teaspoonfuls to 1½ glasses, ¼-½ glass taken 2-3 times a day as an astringent or antihydroticum. The decoction has more tannins.
	The fresh leaf is an aromatic, slightly bitter spice like Camphor and Sage together. In eastern Asia it is used to flavour alcoholic drinks, or as an ingredient in many mixed spices.
Warning	Larger doses — especially of silica — can cause cramps.

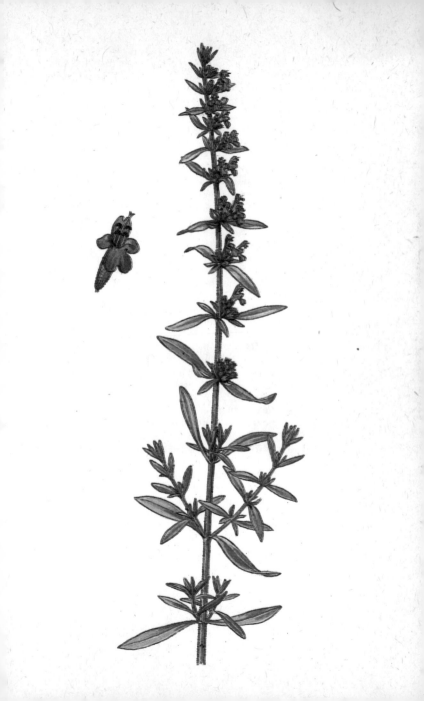

COMMON JUNIPER

Juniper communis
Cupressaceae
Fructus Juniperi — fruit; *Lignum Juniperi* — wood

1-3m (3-10ft) — †† — ‡‡
Flowers: April-May

Botanical description	Spreading, suberect, evergreen shrub or small tree. Narrow needles arranged around the stem in groups of three. The woody plant is dioecious: the male shrub has flowers in the form of little catkins, the inconspicuous female cones ripen into the fruit, globose berries with a blue, waxy bloom.
Habitat	Grows throughout the northern hemisphere on barren ground and pastures, especially at mountain elevations.
Collection	The fruits are collected when ripe by shaking the tree over large canvas sheets, but collection by hand is better. The wood is collected by cutting of small branches.
Drying	Dry in thin layers in the shade. This takes a long time. The wood is dried in the usual way.
Cultivation	Grows in dry, sandy places. Today it is mostly grown because it improves the polluted atmosphere.
Active constituents	Mainly silica with pinenes, then sugars, tannins, flavones, organic acids. The fruits also contain colouring matter. The wood has a small amount of silica.
Efficacy	Diureticum, expectorans, carminativum, stomachicum, cholagogum, antisepticum, derivans.
Use	The diuretic effect is provoked by the direct irritation of the kidneys by silica (or its component terpineol). It has a beneficial effect on the metabolism, stimulates the intestinal peristaltic movements, the secretion of gastric juices and bile, helps flatulence and has considerable antibacterial effects. The silica has similar properties and also improves the blood supply to the skin. The wood is much less effective.
Dosage	The fruits have a fixed dose for the infusion: 0.5g in a warm liquid (don't boil!). Drink by the teaspoonful 2-4 times a day after meals. The silica is added to ointments for rheumatism. The fruits are usually a component of herbal teas with a diuretic effect; therapeutically they are not used by themselves. Wood similarly. The fruit is a popular accompaniment to game.
Warning	Not to be used by people with kidney disorders!

WHITE DEAD-NETTLE

Lamium album
Lamiaceae (Labiatae)
Flores Lamii albi — flower

30-60cm (1-2ft) — ↕
Flowers: April-October

Botanical description	Similar in appearance to the Stinging Nettle. Quadrilateral stem with few branches; opposite, petiolate leaves, ovate and pointed; the flowers are clustered in whorls of 3-5 in the axils of the upper leaves.
Habitat	Nitrogen-loving weed, found along fences, walls, in forest clearings; abundant throughout Europe.
Collection	Only the corollas without the calyx.
Drying	Dry as rapidly as possible to prevent change of colour. Can be dried in the sun or in an oven.
Cultivation	Likes fertile soils containing nitrogen and shady positions; abundant, no need for cultivation.
Active constituents	Mucus, tannins, choline, alkaloid stachydrine, silica, biogenic amines, flavones.
Efficacy	Muciliaginosum, adstringens, antihaemorrhagicum, sedativum, expectorans.
Use	Official medicine uses the drug above all as a mucilage or weak astringent and against bleeding (including excessive menstrual flow). It is also an auxiliary expectorant and in popular medicine a well-known cure for women's disorders, especially painful menstruation (tolerated also by official medicine); for this purpose it is combined with other drugs, and indeed it is never used alone.
Dosage	Usual dose: infusion of 10-20g flowers to 500ml water; drink ½-⅔ glass 2-3 times a day. Popularly used as a so-called 'blood purifying' agent, especially in cases of children's spots, eczema, as well as diarrhoea. Infusions and short decoctions are used externally as gargles for inflammations of the throat, the mouth cavity, etc. When boiled, the tannins also pass into the solution. For this reason the flower, after brief boiling, is used for minor burns, swellings, varicose veins (30g of the drug to 1 litre of water; strain).

MOTHERWORT

50-150cm (1½-6ft) — ‡
Flowers: June-September
Caution

(+) *Leonurus cardiaca*
Lamiaceae (Labiatae)
Herba Leonuri — herbage

Botanical description	The hollow stem is erect, quadrilateral, dark reddish, branching. Dark green palmate leaves with 5-7 segments, very hairy on the underside. The tiny flowers cluster in whorls in the leaf axils.
Habitat	Likes dry meadows, pastures and wasteland. Warmish positions.
Collection	The aerial parts, sometimes also the leaf, are collected in the flowering period.
Drying	Dry in the shade in thin layers.
Cultivation	Sow the seeds in hotbeds in spring or at the end of summer in rows; plant out in the second year. Likes light soils, rich in humus, sunny positions.
Active constituents	Cardenolides, choline, alkaloids, tannins, saponins, flavones and silica.
Efficacy	Cardiacum, hypotonicum, sedativum, stomachicum.
Use	The drug has a tranquillizing effect — for heart disorders, migraine, feelings of anxiety, neuroses, in climacteric, in digestive disorders. Particularly popular in the Soviet Union.
Dosage	Usually an infusion (10-15g of the herbage to a glass of water). Drink in teaspoonfuls in the course of the day. Where it can be used, a decoction of diluted wine is also recommended (for feelings of anxiety, a so-called 'pounding' heart, digestive disorders, climacteric); drink in small glasses. The drug is often included in herbal teas and for heart troubles *(Species cardiacae)*, as a sedative and diuretic. Macerations are not effective enough for heart disorders, which is why extracts are prepared industrially for this purpose (they lengthen the time the heart fills with blood and reduce the pulse rate).
	The hypotensive and sedative effects of the drug are improved by combining it with the root of Valerian and Hawthorn or Camphor.
Warning	Toxic in large doses.

COMMON TOADFLAX

20-60cm (8-24in) — ↕
Flowers: June-October

Linaria vulgaris
Scrophulariaceae
Herba Linariae — herbage

Botanical description	Erect stem, thickly covered with alternate, linear (occasionally lanceolate) leaves, and terminated with clusters of pretty flowers with spurs.
Habitat	Euro-Siberian species — abundant throughout the whole of Europe on pastures and wasteland from lowland to mountain elevations, and in central North America, where it was taken from Europe.
Collection	The herbaceous parts together with the flowers at the beginning of the flowering period.
Drying	The material is dried in thin layers; the colour of the flowers must not change during drying.
Cultivation	Likes loose soils and warm positions.
Active constituents	Mainly flavones, alkaloids, peganine with spasmolytic and peristaltic effects, vitamin C.
Efficacy	Laxans, diureticum, antiphlogisticum, emolliens, cholagogum.
Use	An ancient remedy gradually returning to official medicine. Suitable for various chronic inflammations, atony of the intestines, indigestion, insufficient secretion of the bile into the duodenum, as an auxiliary diuretic. Externally applied to painful, bleeding and badly healing wounds (can be included in ointments).
Dosage	For internal use: a 3-4 per cent infusion (leave to stand 18 minutes), or one teaspoonful of the drug to 2 glases of water, and drink ⅓-½ glass. For external use the usual preparation is a 3 per cent decoction (boil gently about 6 minutes). The drug is usually boiled in milk. For haemorrhoids mix in 2 parts of crushed herbage to 5 parts of pork fat. In popular medicine, it is also applied to oedemas and used to whiten freckles on the face. A strong infusion kills flies.

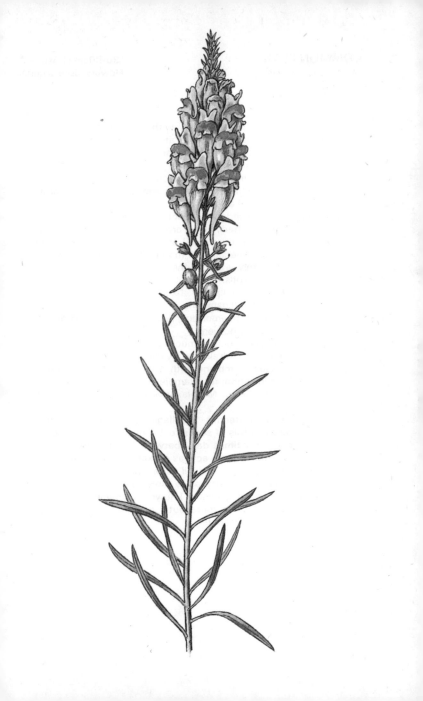

COMMON FLAX

Linum usitatissimum
Linaceae
Semen Lini — seed

30-90cm (1-3ft) — *
Flowers: June-August

Botanical description	Glabrous plant, usually with a single stem, erect at the base and branching at the top; alternate, linear, lanceolate leaves with three veins. Flowers sometimes white, sometimes blue.
Habitat	Probably indigenous to south-western Asia. It has long been cultivated in Europe and North America for its oil (linseed oil) and its fibres.
Collection	The ripe seeds are collected by threshing.
Drying	Dried in a shady place; artificial heat up to 40°C (104°F).
Cultivation	Cultivation over small areas is pointless. Sow early in spring, especially in mountain regions; flax prefers a moderately warm, humid climate and fairly deep, loamy to sandy soils.
Active constituents	Chiefly mucilages, fixed oil, proteins, cyanamide glucosides (linamarine).
Efficacy	Protectivum, emolliens, laxans; oleum: dermatologicum, vehiculum, nutriens.
Use	The seeds, rich in mucilages, are therapeutically most effective in the alimentary canal: the mucilage covers the mucous membrane with a thin layer which protects it from irritation; for example in cases of over-secretion of gastric juices. Mild laxative disinfecting the intestinal tract.
Dosage	As a protective mucilage: a decoction from 1-2 teaspoonfuls of seeds to 1½ glasses of water: drink ½ glass 2-3 times daily between meals. The maceration from this dosage acts as a laxative and is drunk morning and evening. The oil is a cosmetic substance: the unsaturated fatty acids isolated (linoleic, linolenic and others) ard generally known as vitamin F and form a component in therapeutic cosmetics and well-known cosmetic products.

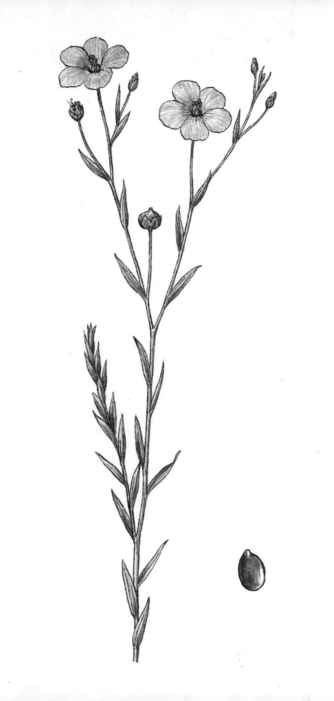

STAGSHORN CLUB MOSS

Lycopodium clavatum
Lycopodiaceae
Lycopodium; Sporae Lycopodii — spores

60-120cm (2-4ft) — ‡
Flowers (spores): June-August

Botanical description	A similar plant to moss: creeping stem with erect forking (dichotomous) branches. Awl-shaped leaves thick on the stems, more spread out on the branches, which usually terminate in spores clustered in the form of spikes.
Habitat	Dry forests from lowland to mountain elevations throughout Europe.
Collection	The ripe spikes are cut off and left to finish ripening, preferably in glass containers in the sun. The spores are then shaken out and sieved; the powder is very light and mobile.
Drying	The pale yellow powder is left to dry.
Cultivation	Cultivation not necessary in Europe, but in most countries this is a protected plant and only collection of the spores is allowed. Prefers acid and silicic soil.
Active constituents	The spores are very rich in fats, then in the high-molecular terpenes similar to cellulose. They also contain acids and traces of alkaloids.
Efficacy	Conspergens; diureticum, urodesinficiens.
Use	Popular medicine uses it for diseases of the urinary tract, liver troubles and similar illnesses. Most frequently, however, it is used externally as a powder sprinkled on wounds, cutaneous eruptions, psoriasis (effect doubtful), furunculosis; an auxiliary dermatological agent.
Dosage	For internal use popular medicine recommends 2 teaspoonfuls of the spores to 2 glasses of water — macerate overnight, drink in gulps in the course of the day; sometimes 1-2g of the spores are taken in wafer form.
	The spores are also put to technical use, as a releasing agent for forms in foundry work, for lighting effects in the theatre, Bengal lights, etc. There are many different types of Club Moss that grow in forests; there is no need to differentiate between them — spores can be collected from all of them. Related species grow in North America.
Warning	The herbage is not collected nowadays on account of its toxicity (except for special purposes). It is dangerous to use it.

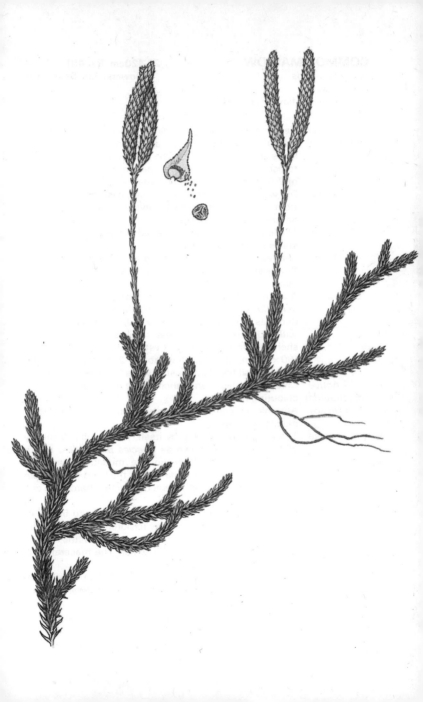

COMMON MALLOW

20-120cm (8in-4ft) — † — ‡
Flowers: July-September

Malva sylvestris
Malvaceae
Flores Malvae —flower; *Folia Malvae* — leaf

Botanical description	Herb with an erect, ascending and very hairy stem. The orbicular petiolate leaves are pinnatilobate with 5-7 lobes and crenate edges. The relatively large flowers (up to 6cm [2 · in] in diameter) on peduncles grow in clusters of 2-6 in the axils of the upper leaves.
Habitat	Dry woodland clearings, meadows, pastures, wasteland, from lowland to foothill elevations in Europe, and naturalized in North America.
Collection	The leaf and flower are collected in the same period, the stalks as short as possible.
Drying	The leaf in the usual way — quickly, in the shade; the flower similarly, but only in one layer; artificial heat to a maximum of 60°C (140°F).
Cultivation	A suitable species for cultivation is *Malva sylvestris* ssp. *mauritiana*; for collection it is cultivated as an annual. Requires loose, loamy to sandy soil, rich in nutrients and with sufficient ground water. Likes sunny positions, sheltered from the wind; best sown in star formation (60×60cm; 2×2ft). Sow about 2cm (1in) deep. By March-April the plant must have its first four leaves.
Active constituents	Chiefly mucilages and tannins. The flower also contains colouring matter.
Efficacy	Antiphlogisticum, protectivum, emolliens, mucilaginosum.
Use	The drug is rarely used by itself; it is combined mainly with herbal teas known as *Species pectorales*, which form a protective layer on the mucous membrane, alleviate a cough, inflammations of the larynx, etc. Often combined with Fennel, Aniseed, Thyme, Chamomile and other drugs.
Dosage	Usually an infusion of 10-15g of the flower to 500ml of water, ½ glass 2-4 times a day (children one teaspoonful every 3 hours). A maceration is made of the leaf: 3 teaspoonfuls to 2 glasses of water. The maceration is also suitable for external use.
Note	For the collection of leaves a related annual-perennial species is of equal therapeutic value — Dwarf Mallow *(Malva neglecta)*.

124

SCENTED MAYWEED, WILD CHAMOMILE 15-50cm (6-18in)
— *

Matricaria chamomilla (M. recutita, Chamomilla recutita)
Asteraceae (Compositae)   **Flowers: May-September**
Flores chamomillae — flower (*Anthodium* — inflorescence)

Botanical description	Glabrous annual plant with a branching stem. Sparce, alternate, amplexicaul leaves, 2-3 times pinnate, linear. The flower-heads have hollow, sharply conical yellow discs, with white rays and a pleasant aroma.
Habitat	Abundant in fields, by the roadside, on waste ground in the countryside in Eurasia, naturalized in the United States and Australia.
Collection	The whole flower head is collected with the shortest possible pedicel; the flowers must not be past their prime or they will disintegrate when dried.
Drying	Dry quickly in thin layers in a well-ventilated place. Artificial heat must not exceed 40-45°C (104-113°F).
Cultivation	The seeds germinate in the light. Chamomile easily adapts to climatic and soil conditions (with the exception of very damp, sandy soils). Sow according to the climate in spring (March-April) where precipitation is at least 50mm (2in) and day temperatures not over 15°C (60°F). The culture must be kept under control, because it can easily overrun surrounding land.
Active constituents	Silica (containing valuable proazulene substances), flavones, sesquiterpenes and coumarins. The mucilage and bitter principles present are also of importance.
Efficacy	Antiphlogisticum, antispasmodicum, carminativum, diaphoreticum, balneologicum, dermatologicum.
Use	The drug can be used alone, but it is often combined in various preparations and herbal teas, sometimes for its aroma. Internally it is used as a disinfectant and antispasmodic, for gastric and intestinal ulcers, etc. Externally it is used for inflammations of the skin and mucous membranes.
Dosage	The usual dose: an infusion of 1-2 teaspoonfuls of the drug to 2 glasses of water, cover and leave to stand about 15 minutes, strain and drink ½ glass three times a day. The infusion can also be used externally for douches, compresses and as a nose swab during hayfever. For baths add an infusion of 150g of the flower heads to half a bathful of water.

RIBBED MELILOT

Melilotus officinalis
Fabaceae (Viciaceae; Papilionaceae)
Herba Meliloti — herbage; *Flores Meliloti* — flower

30-120cm (1-4ft) — † — *
Flowers: June-September

Botanical description	Angular stems, petiolate trifoliate leaves, the leaflets ovoid with dentate edges. Flowers in slender clusters.
Habitat	Warm regions of Central Europe in particular — found on wasteland, embankments, at the edges of fields, in vineyards and gardens.
Collection	The flowering aerial parts are cut off. The flowers by themselves are more rarely collected.
Drying	The material is dried spread out in thin layers in a well-aired place. If artificial heat is used, then not over 40°C (104°F). After drying the drug has a pleasant aroma.
Cultivation	Undemanding, but likes nitrogen in the soil. The seeds can be scattered freely in the vicinity of bee-hives, for example, like clover.
Active constituents	Mainly aromatic coumarins, then mucilages, tannins, flavones, purine substances.
Efficacy	Angiotonicum, anticoagulans, diureticum, spasmolyticum, carminativum; externally: advulnans, detergens.
Use	The drug mildly influences the coagulation of the blood and the tension of the blood vessels. Its diuretic, spasmolytic and carminative efficacy is for the most part claimed by popular medicine, as is its use for insomnia. Allopathy prescribes the drug mainly for compresses. It is often a component of emollient herbal teas, *Species emollientes.*
Dosage	The recommended maximum daily dose for internal use is around 3g, one teaspoonful to a cup of the infusion or maceration; the tea is drunk in small doses during the course of the day. For insomnia 2 teaspoonfuls to 2 glasses of water is the recommended dose.
Warning	Do not exceed the recommended dosage — the drug can cause headaches. Related and similar Melilots are for the most part similarly effective. They are used as an aromatic substance on account of their coumarin odour.

BALM (LEMON BALM)

Melissa officinalis
Lamiaceae (Labiatae)
Folia Melissae — leaf; *Herba Melissae* — herbage

30-80cm (12-32in) — ‡
Flowers: June-August

Botanical description	Quadrangular, branching, hairy stems. Opposite, petiolate leaves, ovate and crenate. White flowers in whorls in the leaf axils.
Habitat	Abundant in the wild in southern Europe (Corsica), North Africa, Asia Minor, the Caucus and in the southern parts of Switzerland. Commonly cultivated, running wild in places.
Collection	The leaf and aerial parts are collected at the beginning of the flowering period.
Drying	Dry by artificial heat up to 35°-40°C (95°-104°F); even better results are achieved with an initial drying heat of 30°C (86°F), gradually increased to 50°C (122°F).
Cultivation	Needs a warm climate, but not sun, does well in half shade. Deep soil rich in humus and nutrients. Dislikes acid soils. The tiny seeds can be sown in spring at the end of March, and planted out in their final position at the end of August. Can also be reproduced vegetatively by dividing 2 - 3-year-old plants. The roots are divided in spring or autumn.
Active constituents	Silica (containing aromatic citral), tannins, bitter principles, triterpenic and organic acids; when ground it has a lemon-like odour.
Efficacy	Nervinium, sedativum, antispasmodicum, stomachicum.
Use	As a sedative for pains and cramps in the stomach and intestines.
Dosage	The leaf (the herbage is used less frequently) is usually mixed with other drugs having a similar therapeutic effect, but it can be used alone. The distillates are very effective and popular (in drops, up to one teaspoonful 3-4 times a day). A very effective drug for migraine and various other pains. Used for baths in cases of nervous stress (the silica can be also used: 2-3 tablespoonfuls).

The leaf is used as a spice for flavouring numerous dishes such as meat and soups.

PEPPERMINT

Mentha × piperita
Lamiaceae (Labiatae)

30-100cm (12-40in) — ‡
Flowers: July-September
Caution

Folia Menthae piperitae — leaf; *Herba Menthae piperitae* — herbage

Botanical description	Quadrangular stem; opposite leaves, lanceolate, pointed, with dentate edges. Flowers in conical terminal spikes.
Habitat	In Europe may be indigenous only to England; naturalized in North America. Long known only in the cultivated form; probably a cross between three species: Water Mint *(Mentha aquatica)*, Apple Mint *(M. rotundifolia)* and Horse Mint *(M. longifolia).*
Collection	The aerial part and the leaf are collected just before flowering.
Drying	Lay out to dry as quickly as possible; best results in drying rooms with artificial heat up to 50°C (122°F). After drying leave a further 6-12 hours to 'breathe' before packing.
Cultivation	Only vegetatively (very rarely from seeds); stolons (underground shoots) should be procured from reliable sources. Best planted out in autumn (October). Requires warm soil rich in humus and supplied with ground water.
Active constituents	Silica (containing menthol), tannins, terpenes, organic acids, bitter principles and flavones.
Efficacy	Carminativum, cholagogum, antisepticum, antispasmodicum, anaesteticum, stomachicum.
Use	For the purposes mentioned above it is often used by itself; as a mouth rinse or gargle it can be combined.
Dosage	Usual dosage of the infusion: a teaspoonful of the leaves to 1-1½ glasses of water; half a glass 2-4 times a day half an hour before meals as a stomachicum. A useful form is the tincture (30-50 drops 2-5 times a day) or so-called peppermint water (1-3 times a day) used as a stomachichum, antianemicum, cholagogum, etc. or for its aroma. Peppermint is an excellent spice used in cooking.
Warning	For little children menthol is a poison!

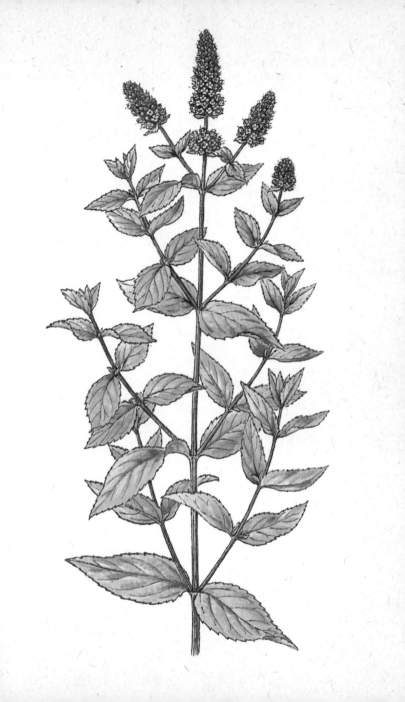

BOGBEAN, BUCK-BEAN

Menyanthes trifoliata
Menyanthaceae
Folia Trifolii fibrini — leaf

15-35cm (6-14in) — ‡
Flowers: May-June

Botanical description	This herb, found in wet bogs, has a creeping underground stem, which sends up large tri-foliate leaves on long petioles, and decorative flowers growing in terminal clusters on erect stalks.
Habitat	Eurasian and North American species; fairly rare and therefore usually completely or partially protected. Grows in peat bogs, watery meadows and marshes.
Collection	Pick carefully by cutting off the leaves without petioles — the roots are easily torn up.
Drying	The leaves dry quickly in thin layers — leafstems are difficult to dry. If artificial heat is used it must not exceed 50°C (122°F).
Cultivation	The plant is becoming increasingly rare. To achieve the best results, cultivate it in its natural habitat: plant out rhizomes about 10cm (4in) long in swampy meadows. Cultivation from seed is a long process.
Active constituents	Therapeutically effective constituents are bitter glycosides *(amara pura)* and flavone compounds (rutin, for example), tannins and iridoids.
Efficacy	Amarum, stomachicum, tonicum, metabolicum, cholagogum.
Use	An ancient remedy for stomach disorders in cases of indigestion and loss of appetite. The leaf used to be soaked in alcohol and drunk in small glasses. Popular use as a nervine, a (weak) cholagogum, or as a metabolicum is not officially recognized by the medical profession — it is unsupported by evidence. It is used mainly for indigestion.
Dosage	The usual dosage of the drug is 0.5g in powder form or an infusion or brief decoction with half a teaspoonful of the drug to a glass of water. 1-2 teaspoonfuls are taken 4-5 times a day half an hour before meals. The drug is usually used as an ingredient in gastric and bitter herbal tea mixtures, in tinctures as well as combined extracts.
Warning	The drug must not be used by pregnant women, and in any case it is unwise to exceed the recommended dosage.

SWEET BASIL

Ocimum basilicum
Lamiaceae (Labiatae)
Herba Basilici — herbage

20-50cm (8-20in) — *
Flowers: June-September

Botanical description	Slender stem, branching at the top. Petiolate leaves, ovate, entire or slightly dentate. The flowers grow in whorl-like fascicles in the axils of scales, together forming terminal spikes.
Habitat	Indigenous to South Arabia. Introduced into Europe in the 16th century from India and Iran, and later to North America.
Collection	Aerial parts are cut off in the flowering period; tied in bundles or dried in layers.
Drying	Dry quickly in the shade at temperatures not over 35°-40°C (95°-104°F).
Cultivation	Requires good garden soil and warm, sheltered sites. Sow in hotbeads in spring (March), when the seedlings are 8-10cm (3-4in) high, plant out in the ground or in flower pots.
Active constituents	Chiefly silica (with aromatic linalol), tannins, organic acids, mineral salts, vitamins and saponins.
Efficacy	Stomachicum, carminativum, aromaticum, antisepticum.
Use	The leaf and aerial parts are popular culinary herbs, usually used fresh; they have a pleasant aroma like cloves and nutmeg together. They have long been used in popular medicine for flatulence, to improve digestion and increase the flow of milk.
Dosage	Make an infusion of 2 teaspoonfuls of the drug to 2 cups of water; one cup twice a day for diseases of the urinary tract and for a cough. Can be used as a gargle and for cleaning wounds. No side-effects — can be added to dietary foods. For medical use it is combined with other drugs having a similar therapeutic effect.
Note	From the medical point of view the plant has not yet been subjected to exhaustive examination. Belief in its efficacy is based only on experience and observation.

SPINY RESTHARROW

30-60cm (1-2ft) — ††

Ononis spinosa   Flowers: June-September

Fabaceae (Viciaceae; Papilionaceae; Leguminosae)

Radix Ononidis — root; *Herba Ononidis* — herbage

Botanical description	Semi-shrub with hairy, thorny branches. Lower leaves trifoliate, upper leaves simple. Symmetrical flowers usually growing singly from the leaf axils.
Habitat	Lowland to foothill elevations throughout Europe, especially on dryish meadows.
Collection	The healthy roots are dug up, the parts growing above the ground are cut off, and the roots quickly washed. On rare occasions the flowering aerial parts are collected.
Drying	The roots are dried in thin layers; if not dried thoroughly they are susceptible to mildew. The aerial parts are dried in the usual way.
Cultivation	Likes warm positions and dryish, loose as well as stony soils, containing lime. Cultivation unnecessary; in some places it grows in rich abundance.
Active constituents	Chiefly silica, flavones, triterpenic acids, tannins, considerable quantities of mineral salts and organic acids.
Efficacy	Diureticum, stomachicum, metabolicum, desinficiens.
Use	Its diuretic effect has been clinically proved and the drug is therefore a component of official diuretic herbal teas; it is weaker though in this respect than the juniper berry. On account of its overall metabolizing effect it can be combined in preparations for rheumatism, gout, skin diseases, etc. Infusions are also used externally for haemorrhoids. Clinical research on the drug and its active constituents has not yet been completed. In popular medicine it is recommended for kidney stones (it acts as a salutericum). It has a weak anti-inflammatory and pain-killing effect.
Dosage	Make an infusion of one teaspoonful of the drug to a glass of water; bring to the boil and simmer covered for 3 minutes, then remove from the heat and leave to stand for 15 minutes, strain and drink ⅓-¼ glass 2-4 times a day. The herbage is used and prepared in a similar way, applied also to badly healing and festering wounds.
Warning	Don't confuse with a similar plant, the unpleasantly smelling *Ononis hircina*, which has a strong odour of goat.

WILD MARJORAM, OREGANO

30-60cm (1-2ft) — ‡
Flowers: July-October

Origanum vulgare
Lamiaceae (Labiatae)
Herba Origani — herbage

Botanical description	Wiry stem, branching towards the top. Petiolate, opposite leaves with ovate blades and entire or dentate edges. Tiny flowers in rich terminal clusters on peduncles in panicle formation.
Habitat	Grows on sunny, grassy slopes, in thickets, copses and forest clearings.
Collection	The flowering aerial parts are cut off and tied up in small bundles to dry.
Cultivation	Requires a sunny position, but can be grown in less fertile soil. Cultivation in fields presents no problems.
Active constituents	Chiefly silica (containing thymol), tannins, bitter principles, mineral substances and vitamin C.
Efficacy	Secretolyticum, spasmolyticum, stomachicum, carminativum, diureticum, diaphoreticum, antisepticum, depurativum.
Use	An old home remedy for headaches and catarrh of the respiratory passages, used as a spice instead of sweet marjoram. The use of the drug has recently been on the decline, but it is now slowly returning to therapy. Sometimes helps with psychical troubles (hysteria). It is also used for gargles, for bathing inflammations, and as an invigorating and aromatic agent.
Dosage	The usual dose is an infusion of a tablespoonful of the drug to 1½ glasses of water; drink ¼ - ½ a glass 2-3 times a day before meals as a stomachic and spasmolytic, after meals as a carminative and expectorant. The silica is not used by itself; it is mixed with Peppermint silica (for cosmetics, soaps, etc.). The herbage is used as a mild spice. It increases the production of bile and gastric juices; add before cooking.

OPIUM POPPY

Papaver somniferum
Papaveraceae

30-150cm (1-5ft) — *
Flowers: June-August
Poisonous plant

Semen Papaveris — seed; + *Fructus Papaveris immaturus* — unripe capsules; *Fructus Papaveris maturus* — ripe capsules; *Folium Papaveris* - leaf; + Opium

Botanical description	Simple, erect stalk; leaves lobate, amplexicaul, glaucous. Large terminal flowers, lilac, white, red or pink. The fruit is in the form of capsules with a large number of seeds.
Habitat	Indigenous to the Orient. In the temperate regions of the world it is generally cultivated for its seeds, which are used in the food industry.
Collection	Good-quality, edible oil is pressed from the seeds. The unripe capsules (poppy heads) are cut through lengthwise and emptied of seeds before drying; the ripe capsules without the seeds are also used. The leaf is collected before the flowering period.
Drying	The drugs are dried in the usual way.
Cultivation	In garden soil in the ordinary way.
Active constituents	The Opium Poppy (a special species of Poppy) contains in all its parts a milky liquid — latex — with about 50 different alkaloids, of which the most important are isolated.
Efficacy	Analgeticum, narcoticum, sedativum, antibechicum, antidiarrhoicum, antispasmodicum.
Use	In view of the serious nature of the plant's efficacy and the fact that it is habit-forming, all preparations are strictly on doctor's prescription and special records of its use are kept. Be warned against the use of ripe or unripe poppy heads as a sedative — cases of poisoning frequently occur!
	Of the alkaloids isolated, the best-known is morphine; which apart from its narcotic effect acts as a pain killer; papaverin relaxes spasms, codein suppresses a cough.
Dosage	Doses are prescribed by the doctor according to the nature and seriousness of the illness.
Warning	The well-known narcotic, opium, is the milk liquid which oozes from unripe poppy heads when incised in a special way.

BURNET SAXIFRAGE

Pimpinella saxifraga

Daucaceae (Umbelliferae; Apiaceae)

Radix Pimpinellae — root; *Herba Pimpinellae* — herbage

15-60cm (6-24in) — ‡

Flowers: June-October

Botanical description	Very polymorphic in appearance. Round stem, almost full, striate. Pinnate leaves with an unequal number of markedly dentate leaflets; the upper leaves are divided into linear segments and have membranous sheaths. Flowers in umbels. Fruit: pendant carpophores. Related species: Greater Burnet Saxifrage *(Pimpinella major)*, equally valuable.
Habitat	Indigenous to Eurasia, from lowland to subalpine vegetational elevations.
Collection	Dig up the subterranean parts, the rhizome and root, in the autumn, or in spring; wash briefly. The aerial parts (rarely required) are cut off during the flowering period.
Drying	The subterranean parts are dried quickly in a well-aired place (artificial temperatures up to 35°-40°C; 95°-104°F); the aerial parts are dried in a similar way.
Cultivation	Likes dryish, loose, calcareous soils; propagated by seed or vegetatively — by dividing the roots of older plants.
Active constituents	Chiefly silica with coumarins, then tannins, saponins and vitamins — especially in the fresh herbage.
Efficacy	Expectorans, spasmolyticum, secretolyticum, diureticum, stomachicum, metabolicum, desinficiens.
Use	For diseases of the respiratory tract it is combined with other drugs. For external use Silverweed rhizome is added. As a home remedy the root was usually macerated in spirits and a small glass drunk on an empty stomach before heavy work, or a tea was made from it for home use.
Dosage	The usual dose is an infusion of one teaspoonful of the drug to a glass of water, 2-3 cups a day, or the drug is added to a glass of water at room temperatures, put over a flame and brought to the boil for 2-3 minutes, left to stand 10-15 minutes and drunk in teaspoonfuls 2-5 times a day. A decoction is also prepared for external use (for gargles, etc.).

The leaf is used as a spice in southern European cooking. An infusion of the herbage (2 teaspoonfuls to one cup) is mainly used as a stomachic and expectorant (one cup 2-3 times a day).

RIBWORT PLANTAIN

Plantago lanceolata
Plantaginaceae
Folia Plantaginis — leaf

10-60cm (4-24in) — ‡
Flowers: May-October

Botanical description	Furrowed scapes. Basal rosette formed of entire, lanceolate, parallel-veined leaves with 3-7 ribs gradually narrowing into petioles. Terminal spike of tiny flowers, ovate or oblong.
Habitat	Nowadays a cosmopolitan species; a hardy weed on dry pastures from lowland to subalpine elevations.
Collection	Only healthy, fresh leaves collected.
Drying	Dry quickly in a well-ventilated place.
Cultivation	Sow only good-quality, selected seeds, about 1cm (½in) deep. Requires rich, fairly damp soils well-supplied with nutriments, nitrogen in particular.
Active constituents	Mainly the iroid aucubine, tannins, pectins, flavones, mineral salts, silicates and vitamin C.
Efficacy	Stomachicum, expectorans, antiphlogisticum, mucilaginosum.
Use	The extracts have antibacterial properties; the aucubine and tannins are therapeutically effective mainly in cases of diarrhoea, inflammations and spasms; they reduce hypaeremia in organs and dilute catarrh. The active principles in Ribwort Plantain also support the secretion of gastric juices. Used externally, they are excellent for wounds; they accelerate granulation, alleviate irritations of the mucous membrane and epidermis.
Dosage	An infusion or decoction of one tablespoonful of the drug to a glass of water; drink half a glass 3-4 times a day; can also be used externally for gargles, compresses, douches, etc. As a stomachic it is combined with Wormwood, Bogbean, Sweet Flag and other drugs. It is an adjuvant in medicaments for ulcers (together with Comfrey, Marsh Mallow, etc.). The syrup (juice) is suitable for children. Recently the seeds of certain species have been used in laxatives.
Warning	This plant should not be confused with related species, which official medicine does not recognize.

COMMON KNOTGRASS

Polygonum aviculare
Polygonaceae
Herba Polygoni avicularis — herbage

10-50cm (4-20in) — * — †
Flowers: June-October

Botanical description	Very polymorphic plant. Slender stems mostly prostrate. Lanceolate, almost linear leaves. One or more inconspicuous flowers of various colours in the leaf axils.
Habitat	Cosmopolitan weed growing in the vicinity of human settlements, in fields, between paving stones and by the roadside.
Collection	The clean flowering aerial parts — wash quickly.
Drying	Dry in thin, well spread-out layers.
Cultivation	A very rapidly spreading weed.
Active constituents	Silicates and their soluble form, silicic acid, flavones, tannins, acids (e.g. caffeinic and chlorogenic), mineral salts, vitamin C.
Efficiency	Diureticum, metabolicum, adstringens, haemostypticum.
Use	Long known as a remedy for diseases of the urinary tract; wastes away sand and small stones, stops bleeding and alleviates colics and catarrhs (usually combined with Silverweed and Ribwort Plantain), an ingredient in many herbal teas. Operates in the basal metabolism — adjuvant in diabetic, expectorant and antidiarrheic preparations.
Dosage	A decoction from 10-20g to 2 glasses of water, half a glass 3 times a day. Can be used for douches, compresses, rinses, etc. Recognized fairly recently by official medicine as an adjuvant in antirheumatic, antisclerotic, biliary and genitourinary herbal teas. Alcoholic extracts prevent the crystallization of mineral substances in the urine and are antiphlogistic, bacteriostatic and diuretic. Research is continuing on the efficacy of the plant in reducing the fragility of blood capilliaries, especially in the alimentary canal.

SILVERWEED

15-50cm (6-20in) — ‡
Flowers: May-June (September)

Potentilla anserina
Rosaceae
Herba Anserinae — herbage; *Radix Anserinae* — root

Botanical description	Stoloniferous herb. Pinnate leaves with an uneven number of sharply serrate soft leaves, with silky hairs on the underside. Solitary flowers growing on long, leafless peduncles from the leaf axils.
Habitat	Common plant on damp pastures, meadows and nitrate soils; grows throughout Europe.
Collection	The flowering aerial parts are cut off, the roots dug up in autumn and quickly washed. The leaves are often mixed in with the drug from the aerial parts, or the leaves are sometimes collected alone.
Drying	Dry in thin layers, quickly. The root is dried in the usual way.
Cultivation	Prefers loamy, loose, nitrogenous soils in dampish positions; abundant in the wild.
Active constituents	Flavones, tannins, bitter principles, vitamin C, mineral salts.
Efficacy	Spasmolyticum, stomachicum, cholagogum, adstringens, antidiarrhoicum, haemostypticum.
Use	Stops diarrhoea; as a spasmolytic especially effective on the smooth muscles of the stomach and intestines (the mechanism of its efficacy is not entirely known, nor the active principle); alleviates spasms accompanying menstruation; increases the secretion of bile, gastric juices. Its effect can be improved by suitable combination: for the stomach, with Centaury . and Peppermint; as a carminative, with Fennel and Angelica; for bile, with Peppermint and White Horehound herbage.
Dosage	The herbage is usually used for a decoction of 1-2 teaspoonfuls to a tablespoonful of the drug to a glass of water, and ¼ - ½ glass is drunk 2-3 times a day. Where the presence of the tannins is not essential, the infusion is preferable (15 mins.) drink 2-3 glasses a day. The decoction is usually made from the root drug; the dosage is the same.
Note	Where therapy requires chiefly the tannins, the rhizome of a related species, Common Tormentil *(Potentilla erecta)* is more suitable; it grows on similar sites.

COWSLIP

15-30cm (6-12in) — ‡
Flowers: March-April

Primula veris, Primula officinalis
Primulaceae
Flores Primulae — flower; *Radix* (Rhizoma) *Primulae* — root (rhizome)

Botanical description	Brown, cylindrical rhizome; basal rosette of elliptic leaves abruptly narrowed below; a central scape terminating in a simple unilateral umbel. Drugs are also collected from a similar, related species, the Oxlip *(Primula elatior)*; there is no need to distinguish between them.
Habitat	Throughout Europe from foothill to alpine elevations on mountain pastures, in thickets and woodlands; not to be confused with the Shooting Star or American Cowslip (genus *Dodecatheon).*
Collection	The flower is usually collected without the calyx. The underground parts are dug up in the autumn and dried in the usual way in a well-ventilated place. Collection of the underground parts is forbidden in most European countries. Only cultivated plants are used.
Drying	Dry quickly and carefully, so that not more than two thirds of the flowers turn green. Well spread out layers and good ventilation (artificial heat up to 35°C; 95°F).
Cultivation	Likes damp places with fertile soil, rich in nutriments, where it can be grown from seed.
Active constituents	The most important are saponins, silica, phenolic glucosides, tannins, sugars; the flower also contains colouring and flavones, but only about ⅓ of the saponins to be found in the root.
Efficacy	Expectorans, metabolicum, diureticum, diaphoreticum.
Use	A very useful medicament for colds, and influenza; a mild diuretic. Clears catarrh from the upper respiratory passages, helps the metabolism in general, therefore suitable for rheumatism, mild neurosis, migraine, nervous disorders accompanied by headaches, mild cases of insomnia. The medical profession gives preference to its efficacy as an expectorant.
Dosage	Flowers: an infusion of 10 teaspoonfuls to 250ml water — the daily dose. Dosages for the rhizome are about one third of those for the flower, as its effect is about three times as strong.

BLACKTHORN, SLOE

Prunus spinosa
Rosaceae

2-3m (6-10ft) — ††
Flowers: March-May

Flores Pruni spinosae — flower; *Fructus Pruni spinosae* — fruit

Botanical description	Thickly branching shrub with black twigs and many stout thorns; small elliptic leaves appearing after the flower, and hairy on the underside of the veins. The numerous flowers literally enveloping the bush. When mature the fruits are blue-black round berries, often remaining on the bush throughout the winter.
Habitat	Sunny positions, open woodland, among rocks from lowland to mountain elevations throughout Europe, and in mountain areas of North America.
Collection	The flower is collected when white, but still in unfurled buds; fruit when really ripe.
Drying	Dry the flower quickly in thin layers; it can even be left in the sun. Easily becomes damp. The fruits are dried by artificial heat (pre-dry in the sun) — don't burn.
Cultivation	Prefers fairly calcareous soils. It can stand heat and dry soils. Often transplated.
Active constituents	The flowers contain mainly flavones, traces of cyanogen glycoside, mineral salts and sugars; the fruits contain tannins, glycosides, organic acids, pectins and sugars.
Efficacy	Flowers. diureticum, diaphoreticum, laxans; fruits: antidiarrhoicum, antiphlogisticum, adstringens.
Use	The flower is a traditional diuretic; it increases the excretion of urine and sodium salts; decreases the fragility and permeability of the walls of the blood capilliaries; has an anti-inflammatory effect; generally increases the excretion of harmful substances and is a mild laxative, therefore also used in children's medicine. The fruits are antidiarrhoeic and anti-inflammatory in effect.
Dosage	Usual dose of flowers: one teaspoonful to a glass of water for a brief decoction: drink ⅓-½ glass 2-3 times a day. The syrup is suitable for children (62g of sugar to 38ml decoction of the flower): take in teaspoonfuls several times a day. The fruits are prescribed for unspecific diarrhoeas (suitable also for children): half a teaspoonful of the fruits is boiled in a glass of water; administer by the teaspoonful 3-4 times a day. The decoction is also suitable for gargles — e.g. in cases of inflammations in the mouth, etc.
General	Sloe is also used to make sloe gin and in liqueurs.

LUNGWORT

Pulmonaria officinalis
Boraginaceae

15-30cm (6-12in) — ‡
Flowers: March-April

Herba Pulmonariae — herbage; *Folia Pulmonariae* — leaf

Botanical description	Herb with short hairs and amplexicaul, broadly lanceolate leaves. Radical leaves petiolate, heart-shaped at the base. The leaves have pale blotches; a related sub-species is without blotches and has soft hairs. Flowers on short peduncles in thick clusters.
Habitat	Favours open woods, especially beech forests. Grows from lowland to mountain elevations almost everywhere in Europe.
Collection	The flowering herbage (the young flowers are pink, changing through red to pale purple and then blue; the inflorescences are therefore multicoloured). Sometimes just the leaf is collected.
Drying	Dry quickly in thin layers.
Cultivation	Prefers shady, damp places and calcareous soils. Sow in the usual way.
Active	Chiefly tannins, alantoin, mucilages, soluble silicates, saponins and mineral salts with a considerable amount of potassium.
Efficacy	Expectorans, mucilaginosum, diureticum, adstringens, antiphlogisticum.
Use	An ancient medicinal plant, tolerated by official medicine. Rarely used by itself; for the above-mentioned purposes it is usually combined: as an expectorant, with Coltsfoot leaf, Aniseed, Fennel, etc.; as a mucilage with Comfrey and Marsh Mallow root; as a diureticum, the drug itself is very weak (it is really a side effect) and therefore it is combined with Silver Birch leaf, Horse-tail, etc., or with drugs containing silicates.
Dosage	A decoction is made of 30 to 60g of the drug to 1 litre of water. Can be used externally, for cleaning cutaneous eruptions, to assist the healing of wounds, haemorrhoids, etc. For internal use: drink ½-0 cup 2-3 times a day.
Caution	Several different plants are called Lungwort in North America, especially the Virginia Cowslip, *Mertensia Virginica*.

COMMON OAK, ENGLISH OAK

20-40cm (65-130ft) — ‡‡

Quercus robur

Flowers: May

Fagaceae

Cortex Quercus — bark; *Glans Quercus* — acorn; *Folia Quercus* — leaf

Botanical description	A tree with alternate, pinnatilobate leaves. Catkin-like flowers; the male flower ripens into an acorn, an ovoid fruit enclosed at the base by a cupule. A related species, the Durmast Oak *(Quercus petraea)*, provides drugs of equal value.
Habitat	Grows on deep, damp soils. Widespread throughout Europe.
Collection	The bark can be collected only with the permission of the owner of the forest. Detach the bark in spring with a stainless steel knife by tapping gently; only the young, thin, shiny mirror bark, not thicker than 5mm (1/5in) is collected. The cupules are removed from the acorns at the time of collection. Collect the leaf only when young and bright green.
Drying	The bark is dried in a well-ventilated place, by artificial heat or in the sun; the acorns and leaves in the usual way.
Active constituents	The bark and leaf contain chiefly tannins, then flavones; the acorn is similar, but starch and sugars prevail.
Efficacy	Bark: adstringens, antidiarrhoicum; acorn: dieteticum, antidiarrhoicum, adstringens; leaf: adstringens.
Use	Official medicine uses the bark only externally, popular medicine uses it internally as well. Externally it is used mainly for slight burns, frostbite, vascular inflammations, eczema; as a gargle for inflammations of the throat, in baths for haemorrhoids, etc.
Dosage	A decoction of the bark (10g of the powdered drug to a glass of water) for compresses, douches, etc. For skin troubles: 3 teaspoonfuls of powdered bark to 500ml water, boil 15 minutes and pour into a bath half-filled with water. Sitz-baths: 50g of the bark and 50g Chamomile to 1 litre water, cover and boil 10 minutes. The leaf is an astringent. The acorns are roasted and used as a coffee substitute.

BLACKCURRANT

Ribes nigrum
Saxifragaceae
Folia Ribis nigri — leaf; *Fructus Ribis nigri* — fruit

120-150cm (4-5ft) — ††
Flowers: April-May

Botanical description	Non-thorny bush, previous year's growth hairy. Alternate, petiolate, palmate leaves. Campanulate flowers always drooping in fairly sparse racemes. Fruits ripen into black berries.
Habitat	Eurasian species; flourishes everywhere, above all in marshy woods from lowland to foothill elevations almost throughout Europe.
Collection	Healthy young green leaves (especially after the flowering period, before the fruits appear); cultivated varieties can also be collected.
Drying	Quickly, in thin layers, well spread out — artificial heat up to 40°-50°C (104°-122°F). The ripe fruits without peduncles are dried only by artificial heat (requires experience).
Cultivation	In the usual way in gardens; likes fresh, damp, loamy non-calcareous soil, supplied with humus. Propagated vegetatively.
Active constituents	Leaf: silica, tannins, flavones, organic acids — including vitamin C — mineral salts; fruit: organic acids, several different vitamins (especially B complex), pectins, sugars and colouring.
Efficacy	Diureticum, diaphoreticum, antisepticum, antidiarrhoicum.
Use	As an adjuvant — most frequently for gout, rheumatism, then as a diureticum (helps the excretion of uric acid), excretes toxic products, harmful metabolites; it is an adjuvant for whooping cough and convulsive coughing. The leaf has recently been put to use by official medicine.
Dosage	A decoction of one tablespoonful of the leaf to a glass of water, ⅓-½ glass 2-3 times a day; a similar decoction is used externally for gargles, mild heat rashes, skin irritations, etc. The fruits are a well-known home remedy for colds, stomach pains and catarrh. Syrup is also prepared from it: gargles for sore throats, mouth inflammations, etc.

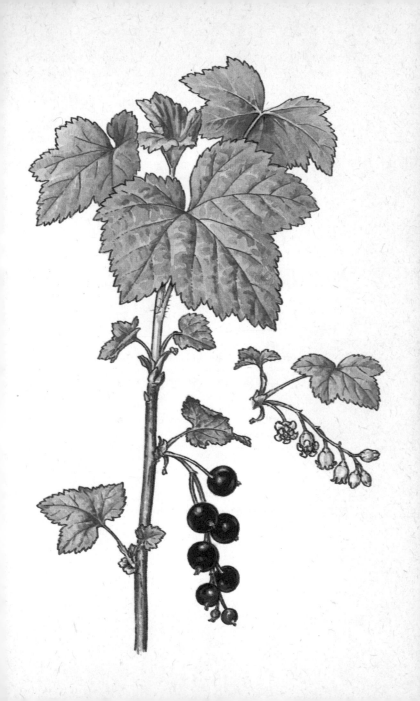

DOG ROSE

1.5-3m (5-10ft) — ††
Flowers: June-July

Rosa canina
Rosaceae
Fructus Cynosbati — fruit; *Semen Cynosbati* — seed (carpophores)

Botanical description	Thorny bush with alternate, pinnate leaves with an uneven number (5-7) of oval or elliptic leaflets, finely dentate. Flowers, solitary or in corymbs of three, terminating the first year's growth. Fruits when ripe: red hips terminating in short hairs.
Habitat	Deciduous woods, shrubland, stony steppe, from lowland to mountain elevations throughout Europe.
Collection	The ripe hips are collected without peduncles before they are damaged by frost. The carpophores are sometimes removed to order.
Drying	In thin layers in a well-aired room. Turn frequently; artificial heat the most suitable (don't burn!). The carpophores and hairs are sometimes also dried, in the usual way.
Cultivation	Usually propagated from cuttings of older bushes. Likes loose soils but grows on almost any soil.
Active constituents	Its vitamin C content is valued above all, carotenoids (vitamin A) are also present, flavones, tannins; the carpophores contain vitamin E in addition to oil and sugar.
Efficacy	Antiscorbuticum, diureticum, cholagogum, tonicum; seed: diureticum.
Use	The hips are used as an adjuvant for many illnesses, e.g. gastric and intestinal ulcers, infectious illnesses, fevers, colds, influenza, for post-operational conditions, etc. For this reason they are included in many herbal teas *(Species cardiacae* — for heart diseases; *Species cholagogae* — for the gall bladder; *Species diureticae* — as a diuretic). Also used alone. The seeds (carpophores) are usually included in diuretic teas.
Dosage	A decoction is usually made of two teaspoonfuls of crushed fruits without seeds to a glass of warm water; boil briefly (for a maximum of 3 minutes), strain. The carpophores are for the most part a diuretic, and popular medicine also recommends them for bladder troubles.

ROSEMARY

50-100cm (20-40in) — ††
Flowers: May-June
Caution

(+) *Rosmarinus officinalis*
Lamiaceae (Labiatae)
(+) *Folia Rosmarini* — leaf; (+) *Herba Rosmarini* — herbage

Botanical description	Evergreen shrub with coriaceous leaves turning under at the edges and with white hairs on the underside. Flowers in whorls in small terminal clusters and in the axils of the leaves.
Habitat	Typical species of Mediterranean flora, planted elsewhere in flower pots or gardens.
Collection	The leaves are stripped from the plant in the flowering period or immediately after; sometimes the non-wooden aerial parts are cut off.
Drying	Dry quickly in a well-aired, shady place; artificial heat not over 35°-40°C (95°-104°F).
Cultivation	Requires a warm, dry climate, sunny, sheltered sites and loose permeable soil with sufficient humus. Sow in hotbeds. Plant out the seedlings at the end of May. At the end of summer they are put in boxes of sand to winter. The following spring (April) plant out 30cm (12in) apart. Protect from frost.
Active constituents	Chiefly silica, flavones, tannins, polymorphic acids, triterpenic compounds, saponins and bitter principles.
Efficacy	Spasmolyticum, stimulans, nervinum, tonicum, derivans.
Use	The drug influences the smooth muscle, relaxes spasms of the urinary tract, gall-bladder and intestines, stimulates the secretion of bile and gastric juices, as well as the peripheral blood circulation (therefore not to be taken during menstruation or by pregnant women). It is also a disinfectant and an aromatic spice. In popular medicine it is also used to improve the blood circulation of the limbs — the legs in particular — in cases of low blood pressure; as a nervine; and for gall stones.
Dosage	Usual dose: an infusion of a teaspoonful of the leaves to a glass of water; drink 3 times a day. The infusion for a bath is 50g to 2 litres of water; pour into a tub half filled with water at 37°C (98°F). Bathe for 10 minutes.
Warning	Large doses should be taken only on the advice of a doctor, for Rosemary then has a toxic effect.

BLACKBERRY, BRAMBLE

1.2-2m (4-6½ ft) — ††
Flowers: June-August

Rubus fruticosus
Rosaceae
Fructus Rubi fruticosi — fruit; *Folia Rubi fruticosi* — leaf

Botanical description	Prickly bush. Leaves have 3-5 oval leaflets markedly dentate at the edges. Flowers in clusters. When ripe the fruits are black berries not separating from the receptacle. Many different but closely related sub-species.
Habitat	At the edge of woods, on meadows and pastures.
Collection	The ripe black fruits are collected in firm containers. Only the young leaf is collected.
Drying	Dry quickly in well spread-out layers. Drying is very difficult and requires experience.
Cultivation	Propagated vegetatively. Likes fairly deep, good soil.
Active constituents	Large amounts of colouring, organic acids, mucilages, pectins and sugars; oil in the seeds. The leaves contain mainly tannins, then flavones, acids — including vitamin C — and mineral salts.
Efficacy	Adstringens, antidiarrhoicum, antiphlogisticum, diureticum, metabolicum.
Use	The juice is used as a home remedy for goitre. Most of the active principles have a stimulating effect on the organism. The drug regulates the growth of beneficial intestinal bacteria. The leaves have a spasmolitic effect, mildly diuretic, and increase resistance to colds and influenza. They are also effective for metabolic troubles — rheumatism, for example. The leaf drug is rarely used by itself, usually as a component of metabolic and antidiarrhoeic teas (e.g. with Raspberry leaf, Bilberries, etc.), and of metabolic teas (with Heartsease herbage, Dog Rose fruits, Dandelion root, etc.).
Dosage	The usual dose of the leaf is a decoction of one tablespoonful of the drug to 1-2 glasses of water; drink ⅓-½ glass 2-3 times a day between meals. The leaf is fermented to make non-alcoholic drinks, or so-called 'home' teas; the fruits are used to make wine.

RASPBERRY

50-120cm (20-48in) — ††
Flowers: May-August

Rubus idaeus
Rosaceae
Folia Rubi idaei — leaf; *Fructus Rubi Idaei* — fruit

Botanical description	Branching, erect bush with fine prickles; pinnate leaves with 3, 5 or 7 ovate leaflets, hairy underneath and dentate at the edge. Flowers in sparse panicles, ripening into red fruits, raspberries, falling away from the receptacle when ripe.
Habitat	Abundant throughout Europe, especially in clearings in pine and beech forests, from lowland to forest elevations; in North America *R. strigosus* is the native species.
Collection	The young, fresh leaves without petioles; ripe fruits are collected in firm containers.
Drying	The leaf in the usual way. Artificial heat and experience are needed to dry the fruit.
Cultivation	Raspberries are propagated vegetatively. They need sufficient moisture and nutriments. Difficult to get rid of.
Active constituents	The leaf contains tannins, flavones, vitamin C, small quantities of silica, mucilate and so-called fruit acids. The fruits have fruit acids, sugars, pectin, mucilage, colouring.
Efficacy	Leaf: adstringens, metabolicum, diureticum, cholagogum, dieteticum; fruit: diaphoreticum.
Use	The leaf has long been used for making tea, for colds as well as everyday use. Vinegar used to be made from raspberry pips by fermenting them in water. Syrup is made from the fruits and serves as a flavouring agent, a drink during fevers, etc. The dried fruits are also added to antipyretic herbal teas (for fevers).
Dosage	A decoction is usually made of the leaves (one tablespoonful to 1½ glasses of water) and ½ glass drunk 3-4 times a day. Used externally for gargles, but usually in combination with similarly effective drugs — often Blackcurrant leaves. An infusion of the fruits is a common diaphoreticum, useful for inflenza and illnesses accompanied by a fever, colds, etc. (drink 2 teaspoonfuls to 1½ glasses of water in the evening; if the patient is allowed, a small dose of rum can be added). An infusion of the fruits can be used when swallowing medicines. The leaves are fermented for use at home or in the food industry (adding aroma and colour).

RUE

+ *Ruta graveolens*
Rutaceae
+ *Herba Rutae* — herbage; *Folia Rutae* — leaf

20-50cm (8-20in) — ‡
Flowers: June-September
Poisonous plant

Botanical description	Glabrous, erect plant, richly branching. Leaves unevenly bipinnate. Radiate flowers on pedicels forming a corymb with oval and oblong petals enclosing the capsule.
Habitat	Indigenous to southern Europe. Cultivated nowadays in all temperate regions.
Collection	The aerial parts are cut off during the flowering period, the leaves are striped from the stalks. Gloves should be worn as the juice often provokes an allergic reaction.
Drying	Quickly, in the shade; if artificially, then not over 40°C (104°F).
Cultivation	Requires a light, calcareous soil, rich in nutrients and a sunny position. Seedlings are grown under glass and then planted out.
Active constituents	Silica with furocoumarins (the cause of allergies) alkaloids, flavones, bitter principles.
Efficacy	Diureticum, spasmolyticum, sedativum, uterotonicum, stomachicum, cholagogum, emmenagogum.
Use	Ever since ancient times Rue has been used as a medicament and a spice; in certain regions it is still sprinkled on bread and butter or meat and macerated in wine and vinegar. It is used as a home remedy for faintness, breathing troubles, hysteria and a 'thudding heart'. It increases the circulation in the abdomen and is therefore not to be taken by pregnant women or during menstruation.
Dosage	A decoction of one teaspoonful of the drug to a glass of water drunk 3-5 times a day; more rarely in doses of 1-2 teaspoonfuls as a spasmoliticum and cholagogum; extracts with water are less effective than those with alcohol (only the less important substances are dissolved in water). More frequently the drug is a component in preparations used for the above-mentioned purposes.
Warning	In general extracts and preparations containing rue should be used only under medical supervision; they can cause heavy menstruation or pigmentation of the skin reacting sensitively to direct sunlight.

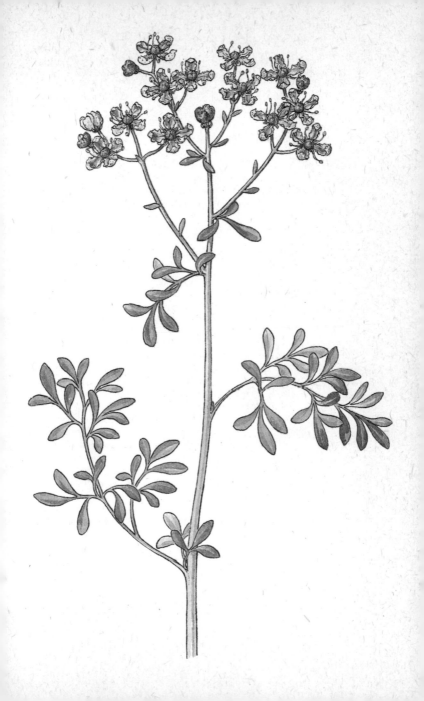

COMMON SAGE, GARDEN SAGE   20-70cm (8-27in) — **
Salvia officinalis   **Flowers: June-July**
Lamiaceae (Labiatae)
Folia Salviae — leaf; *Herba Salviae* — herbage

Botanical description	Semi-shrub with an angular stem becoming woody. The elongated ovate leaves are slightly heart-shaped at the base of the plant. Petiolated flowers in thin clusters. Pleasant aroma.
Habitat	Mediterranean species; now cultivated throughout Europe and North America.
Collection	The leaf and sometimes the aerial parts are collected before flowering.
Drying	Spread out thinly, dry quickly in the shade. Artificial heat 35°-40°C (95°-104°F) maximum.
Cultivation	Prefers dry, limestone soils and sunny positions. Sow the seeds in beds or divide older plants.
Active constituents	Mainly silica, a considerable amount of tannins and pseudotannins, triterpenes, bitter principles, vitamins (the so-called P-factor, permeable, thiamine, nicotinic acid and its amide), an oestrogen derivative and resins.
Efficacy	Antisepticum, antiphlogisticum, stomachicum, antisudorificum, antidiabeticum, ammenagogum, dermatologicum.
Use	Sage is used by itself (as an infusion) for drinking, gargling, washing, compresses, etc. It has a specific antiseptic effect on *Staphylococcus aureus*. The drug is a component of many herbal teas, including those for digestive troubles; it stimulates the production of bile and gastric juices and improves kidney and liver function.
Dosage	An infusion of 5-10g of leaves to a glass of water, to be taken by the teaspoonful 2-4 times a day. Similarly for washing, compresses, etc. For external use 10-15g to a glass of water can be used. Popular medicine recommends it to stop the secretion of milk in nursing mothers and as an antiperspirant (used for baths, too). The leaves are used in small quantities for flavouring.
Warning	The silica is toxic.

COMMON ELDER

3-10m (10-33ft) — ‡‡

Sambucus nigra
Flowers: May-June (July)
Loniceraceae (Caprifoliaceae)
Flores Sambuci — flower; *Fructus Sambuci* — fruit

Botanical description	A shrub with white pith. Pinnate leaves with an uneven number of leaflets. The fragrant flowers form a wide cyme and ripen into black berries.
Habitat	Abundant throughout Europe, northern Asia, and North Africa from lowland mountain elevations. The wild elders of North America are different but related species, but *S. nigra* is cultivated there.
Collection	The flowers are cut off with as short a stalk as possible at the beginning of the flowering period. The fruit is collected when ripe.
Drying	The inflorescences are spread out with their stalks up, or hung up. Dry rapidly in the shade, in a current of air — artificial heat up to 45°C (113°F). The fruits (without stalks) are best dried by artificial heat in one layer (e.g. in the oven — don't burn.
Cultivation	Seedlings are grown in nursery hotbeds. The Common Elder prefers a loose, sandy to loamy soil, rich in humus and relatively damp. Warm, sunny, sheltered positions.
Active constituents	Flowers: flavones, amines, organic acids, silica, tannins, phenols, cyanogenic products of sambunigrine glucoside, mineral salts and a so-far unidentified diaphoretic substance. Fruits: anthocyanide pigments, organic acids, carotenoids, tannins, sugars, silica and a considerable amount of vitamins (B and C), colouring matter.
Efficacy	Flowers: diaphoreticum, diureticum; fruit: diaphoreticum, diureticum, analgeticum, laxans.
Use and dosage	The flowers stimulate secretion of the sweat glands (an infusion of 5-10g to 10ml water), they are an adjuvant for fever, a mild diuretic for children and elderly people in cases of inflammation of the urinary tract and bladder. Antispasmodic effect. Used externally for tonsilitis, etc. The fruits (an infusion of 10-15 to a glass of water) are beneficial for neuralgia and migraine, inflammation of the trifid nerve and sciatica. The analgesic effect is mild, but has been reliably proved.

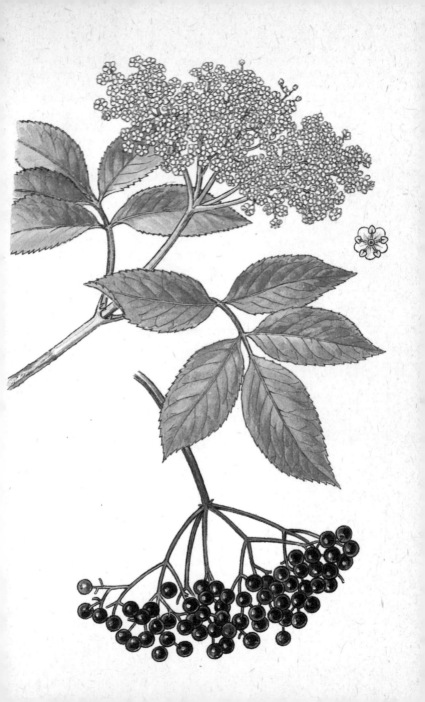

SOAPWORT

30-60cm (1-3ft) — ‡

Saponaria officinalis
Silenaceae (Caryophyllaceae)
Radix Saponariae (rubrae) — root; *Herba Saponariae* (rubrae) — herbage

Flowers: July-September

Botanical description	Erect stem, upper half branching. Large, elongated ovate leaves with three parallel veins. The white or pink flowers form terminal clusters.
Habitat	Along walls, on banks of rivers and streams in Europe and western Asia. Likes damp to wet meadows with loose soil.
Collection	The roots are dug up early in the spring or in autumn. The aerial parts are cut off at the beginning of the flowering period.
Drying	After a quick rinse the roots are dried in a well-ventilated place, possibly in the sun. Artificial heat up to 70°C (158°F). The aerial parts are spread out individually.
Cultivation	Nutritious soil, deep, loose, with sufficient ground water; sunny positions. Sow in August-September in rows about 40cm (15in) apart. Plant out in March-April.
Active constituents	Chiefly the heterosides of triterpenic saponins; the herbage also contains flavones.
Efficacy	Secretolyticum, expectorans, metabolicum, antiphlogisticum.
Use	Similarly effective as the root and rhizome of the Cowslip; the saponins of Soapwort also have mildly antibacterial and good fungistatic effects. They act on the mucuous membranes of the upper respiratory passages and are particularly beneficial for a dry cough. They stimulate the activity of the stomach, intestines, sweat glands, and the metabolic processes in the organism in general. For this reason popular medicine also uses them as a depurative, a diuretic, laxative and to increase the flow of bile. The saponins are also isolated and are added to expectorant preparations in the pharmaceutical industry.
Dosage	A decoction of 2 teaspoonfuls of the drug to 2 glasses of water, 1-2 teaspoonfuls 2-4 times a day. Used externally to prevent the formation of dandruff, loss of hair, for eczema and so on.
Warning	Not to be used over a long period. For internal use the aerial parts are better (less dangerous); for external, the root.

SUMMER SAVORY

Satureia hortensis
Lamiaceae (Labiatae)
Herba Satureiae — herbage

20-30cm (8-12in) — *
Flowers: June-September

Botanical description	Aromatic herb with a branching stem. Leaves amplexicaul or on short petioles, slenderly lanceolate, spotted with glands. Branches bearing 1-5 flower whorls growing out of the leaf axils on the upper half of the stem.
Habitat	Grows in the wild in southern Europe, cultivated elsewhere.
Collection	The flowering aerial parts are collected, or the leaves together with the flowers.
Drying	Dry in the usual way immediately after collection: in the shade, quickly; artificial heat up to 35°C.
Cultivation	Easily grown in good garden soil or in flowerpots; it needs a warm, sunny position. Sow in spring in rows about 20cm (8in) apart.
Active constituents	Chiefly silica, containing principally cymene, carvacrol and pinene, then tannins, mucilage and mineral salts.
Efficacy	Stomachicum, carminativum, adstringens, antisepticum.
Use	The therapeutic aspects of Summer Savory are not very marked, and therefore in many countries it is regarded more as a culinary herb. It increases the secretion of gastric juices, relaxes tension in the smooth muscle of the biliary passages, urinal and alimentary organs (especially the intestines), regulates peristalsis, has a mild antidiarrhoeic effect and antibacterial and anti-inflammatory properties. The silica also has an anthelmintic effect (one account of the carvacrol content). Rarely used alone.
Dosage	An infusion (10g herbage to a glass of water) is drunk 2-3 times a day by the ¼ glass as a carminative and stomachicum, ⅓-½ glass as an antidiarrhoeic. Decoctions contain less silica than infusions.

In cooking Savory is used mainly in fatty dishes and is especially suitable for vegetables and poultry.

GOLDEN ROD

60-100cm (24-40in) — ‡
Flowers: July-September
(October)

Solidago virgaurea
Asteraceae (Compositae)
Herba Solidaginis — herbage

Botanical description	Erect stem; narrow leaves, the lower ones narrowing into long petioles, the upper with short petioles, dentate edges. Leaves in the inflorescence amplexicaul. Flower bracts in many rows with slender outer petals. the numerous flowerheads form an oblong panicle.
Habitat	Throughout Europe, from lowland to mountain elevations as a circumpolar species. Open woods and woodland clearings, heaths, by the wayside and along walls. About 100 related species grow in North America.
Collection	The aerial parts are cut off at the beginning of the flowering period.
Drying	Dry in small bundles or in very thin layers. Tends to crumble and become damp.
Cultivation	Prefers loose, fairly calcareous soils.
Active constituents	Chiefly flavones, rutin in particular, then tannins, polyphenolic acids (pseudotannins), silica and saponins.
Efficacy	Adstringens, diureticum, antiphlogisticum.
Use	A plant frequently used in popular medicine. Very effective, especially the alcohol extracts, as a diuretic, for the excretion of bile, and for haemorrhages, decreases the fragility of capilliaries. Applied to wounds, used for inflammations and stones in the urinary tract, as as adjuvant for rheumatism, ulcers in the alimentary organs, gastric catarrh, minor internal haemorrhages and excessive fermentation. The drug is usually combined or the active substances extracted.
Dosage	Usually an infusion (one teaspoonful of herbage to 1½ glasses of water); drink ¼ - ½ glass 2-3 times between meals (especially as a diureticum, depurative). For external use decoctions are mostly used (one to two teaspoonfuls to 1½ glasses of water — boil about 3 minutes). Used as a gargle for inflammations of the throat, of the mouth cavity, also for washing, swabs and douches. Up to a 10 per cent decoction can be made.
Note	The American species Late or Giant Golden Rod, *Solidago gigantea*, and Tall or Canadian Golden Rod, *Solidago canadensis* can also be used as drugs.

COMMON COMFREY

Symphytum officinalis
Boraginaceae

30-100cm (12-20in) — ‡
Flowers: May-September

Radix Symphyti — root; *Folia Symphyti* — leaf; *Herba Symphyti* — herbage

Botanical description	Robust polymorphic plant. Long, thick, sometimes branching roots growing out of thick rhizomes. Branching stem winged with decurrent, alternate, ovately lanceolate leaves. The whole plant is roughly hairy. Flowers in drooping terminal clusters of 5-20 bell-shaped corollas.
Habitat	Abundant throughout the whole of Europe from lowland to foothill elevations; grows in meadows, ditches, on embankments, by the wayside.
Collection	The root is dug up in autumn. The leaf and herbage are picked in the flowering period.
Drying	Dry the leaf and herbage quickly in thin layers. The root is slow to dry; it is also used fresh.
Cultivation	Likes damp to wet soil, rich in nitrogen.
Active constituents	The most therapeutically active substance is alantoin, then mucilage and tannins.
Efficacy	Advulnans, antiphlogisticum, protectivum, mucilaginosum.
Use	Cleans and heals wounds, helps the formation of new tissue joining fractured bones (advulnans) and reduces inflammations. A protective agent for ulcers or externally for scalds, frostbite, etc. Traditionally used for lung diseases and dermatitis.
Dosage	For internal use: drink 2-3 cups of about 5 per cent infusion a day. For external use the juice is mixed into ointments. For ulcers it is used as a stimulant and protective agent: prepare a decoction of one teaspoonful of the root to 1½ glasses of water, macerate overnight, in the morning bring to the boil for 1-2 minutes, strain and drink ½ glass twice a day; in cases of poorly-healing fractures this maceration is applied externally. Syrup is also made from the root, or pure alantoin is isolated and used as an ingredient in powders or ointments. More recently the root has been recommended for rheumatism, neuralgia, bronchitis, pleurisy and in official medicine as a mild laxative.

TANSY
60-130cm (24-50in) — ‡

+ *Tanacetum vulgare;* syn.: *Chrysanthemum vulgare*

Flowers: July-September

Asteraceae (Compositae)

Poisonous plant

+ *Flores Tanaceti* — inflorescence; + *Folia Tanaceti* — leaf; + *Herba Tanaceti* — herbage

Botanical description	Erect, tough stem, somewhat angular, rarely branching. Alternate, pinnate leaves. Small pedunculated flowers in corymb formation.
Habitat	Very frequent throughout the whole of Europe, by the wayside, on embankments, near streams, at the edge of woods — from lowland to mountain elevations. Often grown in gardens as a decorative variety with curly leaves.
Collection	Inflorescences without petioles, the leaf and flowering part of the herbage.
Drying	Dry quickly.
Cultivation	Prefers loose soil rich in nutrients. In gardens a related species is more often grown, *Chrysanthemum balsamita,* which smells like balsam (balm).
Active constituents	The main constituent is silica (in Central Europe most frequently toxic thuyone), then flavones, bitter principles, tannins and, in the root, inulin.
Efficacy	Vermifugum, antipediculosum (against lice).
Use	An ancient medicinal plant; its efficacy as a vermifuge against parasites such as intestinal worms and lice is due to the thuyone content in the silica. The inflorescences are not suitable as a stomachic or emmenogogue or for little children, pregnant women or elderly people, nor for those with ulcers.
Dosage	Vermifuge for adults: 5-10g of powdered inflorescences in jam, ricin oil as a laxative after 2-3 hours; use in two doses for a period of 4-5 days. Or: an infusion of a teaspoonful of the flowers to a glass of water; drink one glass twice a day for 3-4 days. The mode of use will be prescribed by the doctor. For parasites in the hair: wash the hair with an infusion of 2 teaspoonfuls of the drug to a glass of water, cover it with a scarf for 2-3 hours, wash again and comb out. After 24 hours wash the hair with warm diluted vinegar and comb out again. Repeat after 6-7 days. The herbage can be used in small quantities as a spice.
Warning	The drug from the aerial parts is misused to cover the smell of stale food. Overdoses of this drug may be fatal.

DANDELION

10-60cm (4-24in) — ‡
Flowers: April-October

Taraxacum officinale
Asteraceae (Compositae)
Radix Taraxaci — root; *Radix Taraxaci cum herba* — root with herbage;
Folia Taraxaci — leaf; *Flores Taraxaci* — inflorescence

Botanical description	Branching rhizome; long, branching root, which like the whole plant exudes a milky juice (latex). Radical roots in rosette formation with tooth-like lobes; fragile hollow scapes terminating in largish inflorescences made up of numerous fine petals and long, recurved bracts; fruit: carpophores mounted on white tufts.
Habitat	Found practically everywhere from lowland to fairly high elevations throughout Europe, introduced to North America. Very polymorphic in appearance.
Collection	The root is dug up in autumn or early spring. The root together with the herbage in spring, when the plant has only buds; dried where possible by artificial heat. The young, healthy leaves dry quickly. The inflorescences are boiled fresh to make syrup or dried quickly.
Cultivation	For pharmaceutical use it must not be cultivated; this decreases the amount of therapeutically effective bitter principles.
Efficacy	Cholagogum, diureticum, stomachicum, metabolicum.
Use	The root is thought to act as a diuretic, but the flower is more efficacious in this respect.
Dosage	One teaspoonful of root drug to 1½ glasses of warm water; bring slowly to the boil and simmer gently 5 minutes, leave to stand 10 minutes, strain. Drink ½ glass 2-3 times a day 15 minutes before meals. To stimulate the flow of bile it is usually combined with Peppermint, Greater Celandine and Wormwood; as a diuretic with Birch leaf, Parsley, Horse-tail, etc.; as a stomachic with Gentian root, Wormwood, Bogbean; its antidiabetic effect is increased by the addition of Bilberry leaf, Goat's Rue, etc. The dosage for the flower is similar; infusions are best made when mixed with equal quantities of the root. Recently the inflorescences have come to be used for cough syrup.

WILD THYME

Thymus serpyllum
Lamiaceae (Labiatae)
Herba Serpylli — herbage

5-30cm (2-12in) — ‡
Flowers: April-September

Botanical description	Creeping, even decumbent, stem, woody at the base. Small, elliptic, rather leathery (coriaceous) leaves, fragrant when crushed. Flowers in the leaf axils, in whorls of 3-6. Very polymorphic species.
Habitat	Very abundant throughout the whole of Europe — between fields, by the roadside, on hillsides, in dry meadows.
Collection	The flowering herb at the beginning of the flowering period, without roots and grass. Dried in thin layers, well spread out. Unsuitable for collection when in full bloom.
Cultivation	Prefers loose but dry, permeable soil, rich in nutrients. Sow out in the ground or in hotbeds; the seedlings planted out when 5-7cm.
Active constituents	Mainly silica (0.15-0.6 per cent) of varying composition, then tannins, bitter principles, flavones and mineral salts.
Efficacy	Antisepticum, expectorans, stomachicum, aromaticum.
Use	Its efficacy lies mainly in the silica — thymol and carvacrol determine its protibacterial effect — therefore used in stomatology as a mouthwash for stomatitis, for compresses and aromatic baths. A very good expectorant, stomachic and spice.
Dosage	An infusion of one teaspoonful of the herbage to 1½ glasses of water, leave covered 20 minutes, strain and drink ½ glass 3-4 times a day 30 minutes before meals as a stomachic; after meals as a carminative, expectorant or antiseptic. An infusion of 2½ teaspoonfuls to 2 glasses water, leave to stand 15 minutes; for gargles, mouth washes, compresses can be combined with Chamomile flowers, Sage leaf, Ribbed Melilot herbage, etc.; for tampons with Plantain leaf, Linden flower, Walnut leaf, the many-petalled flowers of the Pot Marigold *(Calendula officinalis)*, Yarrow inflorescences, etc. For baths: an infusion or decoction of 200g drug to 3 litres water; strain and pour into half a bathful of water at 37°-38°C (98°-100°F) and bathe for 10-20 minutes (according to age and state of health), for convalescence, elderly people, and so on.

GARDEN THYME

Thymus vulgaris
Lamiaceae (Labiatae)
Herba Thymi — herbage

30-40cm (12-15in) — ‡
Flowers: May-June

Botanical description	Thickly branching semi-shrub with quadrilateral stems and small opposite lanceolate or oblong leaves, hairy on the underside. Flowers in whorls.
Habitat	Species indigenous to the Mediterranen region, widely grown in gardens and flower-pots.
Collection	The leaves and flowering top parts are collected at the beginning of the flowering period.
Drying	Dry quickly in thin layers.
Cultivation	Prefers good, light soil; warm, sunny positions. Must be sheltered from the wind or the frost will kill it. Sow in hotbeds to prepare seedlings.
Active constituents	The main therapeutically effective substance is the silica, containing thymol with its disinfectant properties. Tannins, flavones, organic acids, triterpenes and bitter principles are also present.
Efficacy	Antisepticum, antibechicum, stomachicum, anthelminticum, expectorans, aromaticum, adstringens.
Use	An excellent expectorant (2-3 per cent infusion, leave to stand 10 minutes, 2-3 cups a day), facilitates the secretion of mucus, also acts as a spasmolytic; suitable for whooping cough and inflammations of the upper respiratory passages. Effective for stomach ulcers, insufficient secretion of gastric juice, and as a carminative. The silica is prescribed for external use only as a rubefacient, antiphlogistic, antiseptic and, on account of its thymol content, sometimes as a vermifuge (mode of use determined by the doctor).
Dosage	An infusion is usually made of one teaspoonful of the drug to 1½ glasses of water, ⅓ glass drunk 3 times a day as a stomachic (before meals) and as an expectorant after meals. For washing children (to get rid of lice, etc.): 15g Thyme and 10g Tansy flowers to one litre of boiling water, cover and leave to steam, then use in the bath. An invigorating bath is prepared from a decoction of 200g Thyme to half a bath of water at 37-38°C; bathe for 10-15 minutes. The decoction can also be used for compresses and as a hair tonic for thinning hair and dandruff.

BROAD-LEAVED LIME, LINDEN

Tilia platyphyllos
Tiliaceae
Flores Tiliae — flower

up to 40m (130ft) — ‡‡
Flowers: June-July

Botanical description	Tall, thickly branching tree with large, roundly cordate leaves, light green with white hairs below, dark green on the upper side. Corymbs of 3-9 flowers.
Habitat	Abundant in Europe, especially on rocks and wasteland at hilly and mountain elevations. Related species are native to North America — see *Note* at end.
Collection	The whole inflorescence together with the membranous bract is picked before the flowers are in full bloom.
Drying	Dry in thin layers as quickly as possible in order to preserve the original colour of the bract.
Cultivation	Prefers deep, fertile soil. Propagated from seeds or vegatatively.
Active constituents	Flavones, organic acids, triterpenes, a small quantity of mucilage and tannins, silica containing farnesol, sugars and some vitamins.
Efficacy	Diaphoreticum, sedativum, cholagogum, spasmolyticum, diureticum, stomachicum.
Use	Most commonly used for chills to provoke sweating; an infusion or brief decoction, sweetened with honey. Also prescribed for inflammations of the upper respiratory passages, tonsilitis, etc. A component in herbal teas for neurosis, neurasthenia; it is used for gargles and it is a very good cosmetic for cleaning the complexion, in addition to having aromatic properties.
Dosage	The infusion is made from one teaspoonful of the flowers to ⅔ glass water and drunk in half glasses 2-4 times a day as a stomachic and spasmolytic. Prepared similarly, but drunk hot before going to bed, serves as a diaphoretic. Laxative herbal teas usually include Lime flowers to alleviate spasms. Also an ingredient in slimming teas. The decoction can be applied to the face as a compress.
Note	Equally efficacious are the flowers of a related European species, Small-leaved Lime, *Tilia cordata,* which has inflorescences of 3-16 flowers and smaller leaves. Other species of Lime are rarely used.

itae)

lorescence; *Folia Farfarae* — leaf

, creeping, scaly rhizomes. Stem terminating in a
e flower with many rays. Cordate, shallowly lobate
es on long petioles appearing after flowering.

y common European species from lowland to
alpine elevations; abundant in ditches, on
bankments, in uncultivated places. Introduced into
rth America.

florescences with as short a stem as possible; not
itable when in full bloom. Only healthy, undamaged,
ean leaves.

ry flowers quickly — thin layers, maximum 1cm (½in).
eaves in a single layer, stalk up.

Propagated vegetatively.

First of all mucilage, then tannins, silica, carotenes,
organic acids, sugars; the inflorescences also contain
flavones, bitter principles and large quantities of mineral
salts.

Mucilaginosum, adstringens, spasmolyticum.

The inflorescences and leaf are known for their
mucilaginous effect: they cover the mucous membrane
with a protective film, which in the upper respiratory
passages reduces irritation, while the tannins have an
astringent and anti-inflammatory effect, relieve
congestion, destroy bacterial flora, and the flavones relax
spasms. The flower and the leaf with their mineral salts
— zinc in particular — stimulate the function of the
internal glands (the production of insulin, for example).

ge Usually 2 teaspoonfuls of the drug to a cup of infusion —
drink 2-4 cups a day. For compresses and gargles a brief
decoction is prepared of 10-15g of the leaves to 2 glasses
water; inflorescences in an infusion for compresses
applied to skin irritations (from the sun as well), or a brief
decoction, 3-4 minutes, of one teaspoonful of the
inflorescences is drunk 2-3 times a day between meals
as an expectorant or protective agent. It can also be used
externally: the drugs are a cosmetic for greasy skin.
Rarely used by itself.

arning Do not confuse it with similar species of *Petasites*
(Butterburs) which have larger leaves.

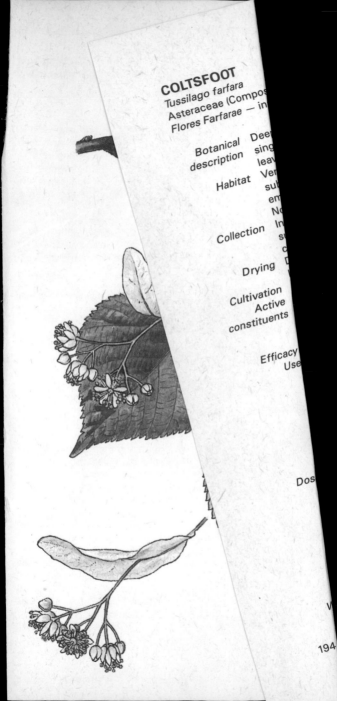

COLTSFOOT
Tussilago farfara
Asteraceae (Compos...
Flores Farfarae — in...

Botanical description	Dee... sing... leav...
Habitat	Ver... sub... em... No...
Collection	In... s... o...
Drying	D... v...
Cultivation	
Active constituents	
Efficacy	
Use	
Dos...	

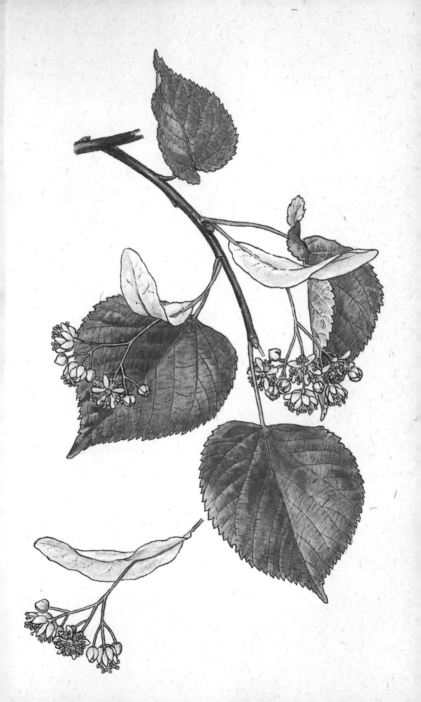

COLTSFOOT

10-30cm (4-12in) — ‡
Flowers: March-April

Tussilago farfara
Asteraceae (Compositae)
Flores Farfarae — inflorescence; *Folia Farfarae* — leaf

Botanical description	Deep, creeping, scaly rhizomes. Stem terminating in a single flower with many rays. Cordate, shallowly lobate leaves on long petioles appearing after flowering.
Habitat	Very common European species from lowland to subalpine elevations; abundant in ditches, on embankments, in uncultivated places. Introduced into North America.
Collection	Inflorescences with as short a stem as possible; not suitable when in full bloom. Only healthy, undamaged, clean leaves.
Drying	Dry flowers quickly — thin layers, maximum 1cm (½in). Leaves in a single layer, stalk up.
Cultivation	Propagated vegetatively.
Active constituents	First of all mucilage, then tannins, silica, carotenes, organic acids, sugars; the inflorescences also contain flavones, bitter principles and large quantities of mineral salts.
Efficacy	Mucilaginosum, adstringens, spasmolyticum.
Use	The inflorescences and leaf are known for their mucilaginous effect: they cover the mucous membrane with a protective film, which in the upper respiratory passages reduces irritation, while the tannins have an astringent and anti-inflammatory effect, relieve congestion, destroy bacterial flora, and the flavones relax spasms. The flower and the leaf with their mineral salts — zinc in particular — stimulate the function of the internal glands (the production of insulin, for example).
Dosage	Usually 2 teaspoonfuls of the drug to a cup of infusion — drink 2-4 cups a day. For compresses and gargles a brief decoction is prepared of 10-15g of the leaves to 2 glasses water; inflorescences in an infusion for compresses applied to skin irritations (from the sun as well), or a brief decoction, 3-4 minutes, of one teaspoonful of the inflorescences is drunk 2-3 times a day between meals as an expectorant or protective agent. It can also be used externally: the drugs are a cosmetic for greasy skin. Rarely used by itself.
Warning	Do not confuse it with similar species of *Petasites* (Butterburs) which have larger leaves.

STINGING NETTLE

(+) *Urtica dioica*
Urticaceae

60-150cm (2-5ft) — ↕
Flowers: June-October
Caution

(+) *Herba Urticae* — herbage; + *Folia Urticae* — leaf; (+) *Radix Urticae* — root

Botanical description	A coarse plant covered with stinging hairs. Usually dioecious. Erect stem, quadrilateral. Leaves cordate, almost lanceolate, roughly dentate. Thin catkins of tiny green flowers growing from leaf axils.
Habitat	Widespread and abundant throughout Europe in woodland clearings, on wasteland as well as cultivated land; introduced into North America.
Collection	The aerial parts are collected before flowering — only the young, leafy tops of the plant. The root is dug up in spring or autumn.
Drying	The leaf dries quickly (artificial heat up to 60°C; 140°F). The root must be dried in a well-ventilated place.
Cultivation	Likes damp soil containing nitrogen; abundant, no need for cultivation.
Active constituents	Leaf: chiefly mineral salts, carotenoids, flavones, a large amount of chlorophyll, some vitamins and substances lowering the level of sugar in the blood. The stinging hairs contain an unknown toxic substance which causes blisters. The aerial parts contain similar substances, and the root more tannins than the leaf.
Efficacy	Diureticum, metabolicum, antidiarrhoicum, haemostypticum, antisepticum, derivans.
Use	Popularly believed to purify the blood, stops bleeding, cures rheumatism by its stinging action. The young leaves are boiled gently like spinach as a nutritious dish. Used as a hair rinse.
Dosage	The leaf is above all a diuretic (encouraging the excretion from the organism of various salts), a depurative and metabolic; the dosage is a decoction of half a teaspoonful to a glass of water. Drink ¼ glass several times a day. Rarely used alone. The root is put to similar use: a decoction of one teaspoonful of the drug to 1½ glasses of water. Serves as an astringent. Also used as a hair rinse for falling hair and to cure dandruff.
Note	A related annual, the Small Nettle *(Urtica urens)* has similar active principles.

BILBERRY, BLUEBERRY, WHORTLEBERRY 15-40cm (6-18in)
_ **

Vaccinium myrtillus   **Flowers: May-June**
Ericaceae
Folia Myrtilli — leaf; *Fructus Myrtilli* — fruit

Botanical description	Thickly branching, low shrub. Angular stems and ovate, acute, deciduous leaves. The flowers ripen into bluish-black berries, borne singly.
Habitat	Abundant throughout Eurasia, especially on poor soils at higher, sometimes even alpine elevations. Related species grow in North America; they bear their fruit in clusters.
Collection	The leaves are stripped from the stalks before the flowering period. The fruits can be collected in firm containers using special combs.
Drying	Dry the leaves quickly in thin layers. Fruits dried only by artificial heat.
Cultivation	Prefers acid, non-calcareous soils. Buy from specialists.
Active constituents	Fruit: mainly tannins, a mixture of pigments (anthocyanins, etc.), organic acids, pectins, sugars and vitamins. Leaf: similar constituents, plus flavones, triterpenes and free hydroquinone.
Efficacy	Fruit: adstringens, antisepticum. Leaf: antidiabeticum, diureticum, desinficiens.
Use	Bilberries improve nocturnal sight and strengthen the blood capilliaries. The fruits are a very effective antidiarrhoeic (especially for children), excellent for chronic dyspepsia, infections of the mucous membranes in the larynx, as well as for eczema (externally). The leaf is included in antidiabetic herbal teas; in cases of inflammations of the urinary tract it increases the flow of urine and has bacteriostatic and anti-inflammatory properties.
Dosage	A decoction of the fruits (10-15g to 250ml water) is drunk ⅓-¼ glasses 2-3 times a day; as a diuretic an infusion of the leaves is made (20-30g to 500ml water), drink ½ glass 2-3 times a day; for diabetes it is usually combined with Goat's Rue herbage and Bean pericarps; a decoction of the fruits is used as a gargle. It has been discovered that the fruits contain two thermolabile substances soluble in water, active against *Escherichi coli* and certain staphylococci; for this purpose an infusion (not a decoction) of the fruits should be made. The fruits are the most healthy of the forest fruits.

COWBERRY

Vaccinium vitis-idaea
Ericaceae
Folium vitis idaeae — leaf; *Fructus vitis idaeae* — fruit

10-30cm (4-12in) — * *
Flowers: May-August

Botanical description	Low evergreen shrub with scaly, creeping runners. Elliptic, coriaceous leaves dotted brown beneath, margins involute. Flowers in terminal clusters maturing into round scarlet berries.
Habitat	Species of the forest, scattered throughout central and northern Europe, often forming brakes, from foothill to alpine elevations. Cranberries, such as *V. oxycoccus,* are closely related.
Collection	The leaf is stripped off the stalk; the fruit collected when ripe.
Drying	Dry the leaf in thin layers. The fruit is rarely dried.
Cultivation	Undemanding as regards nutriments and water; grows even on poor ground, but prefers acid soil.
Active constituents	The leaves are rich in phenolic glycosides; they also contain tannins, flavones and mineral salts. The fruit: anthyocyanins, carotenoids, tannins, organic acids, vitamin C, sugars, pectin and colouring.
Efficacy	Leaf: urodesinficiens, salutericum, adstringens. Fruit: adstringens, dieteticum.
Use	The leaf is above all a disinfectant and anti-inflammatory agent of the urinary tract, a diuretic. The fruit is also of dietary value, owing mainly to its high vitamin C content. The flavones and anthocyanins help to strengthen the wall of the blood capilliaries.
Dosage	Usual dosage of the leaf: 1½ teaspoonfuls to a glass of water, boil gently about 5 minutes; drink ⅓ to ½ glass 2-3 times a day. Also effective to increase the flow of bile; the daily dose can be up to 10g. The fruits act as a dietetic and to strengthen the blood capilliaries: a decoction of one teaspoonful to a glass of water, drunk 2-3 times a day between meals.
Warning	Cowberries contain a considerable amount of oxalic acid, which is very difficult to eliminate from the body.

COMMON VALERIAN

Valeriana officinalis
Valerianaceae
Radix Valerianae — root; *Herba Valerianae* — herbage

30-70cm (12-27in) — ‡
Flowers: July-September

Botanical description	Robust herb with a short, creeping rhizome, covered with many tiny roots. Pinnate leaves; tiny sessile flowers in large terminal clusters forming a corymb.
Habitat	Damp meadows, river banks, shrub-covered slopes from lowland to mountain elevations in Europe; cultivated in North America.
Collection	Subterranean parts: the root is dug up in autumn, or sometimes in May, and dried quickly in a well-ventilated place isolated from other plants. The aerial parts are picked during the flowering season and dried in the usual way.
Cultivation	Light, loamy to sandy soils with sufficient nutrients are the most suitable. Grows well in valleys. Best results achieved with seedlings, sown out in February, but can be sown in boxes in autumn and left outside in the frost. Seedlings hardened in this way are sown out in the damp spring soil.
Active constituents	The root and aerial parts have more or less the same: mainly silica, esters, organic acids, alkaloids, acetylenic compounds, known as valerianic (special esters).
Efficacy	Sedativum, spasmolyticum.
Use	A well-known sedative. Alleviates spasms, suppresses irritation, but removes tiredness. The powdered drug and alcoholic extracts are the most effective forms.
Dosage	The traditional herbal tea is prepared as an infusion of one teaspoonful of the drug (5 per cent) and drunk by the cup several times a day. The silica can also be used, 10 to 20 drops 3-4 times a day. The most convenient form is the tincture (which can be bought), 10-20 drops in water.

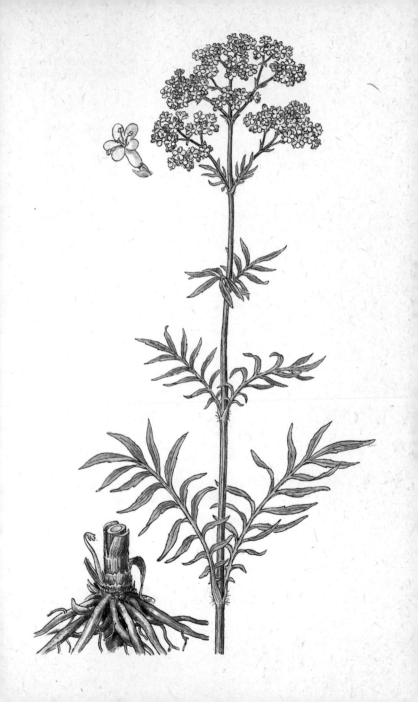

VERVAIN

Verbena officinalis
Verbenaceae
Herba Verbenae — herbage

30-70cm (12-27in) — ‡
Flowers: July-October

Botanical description	Stem tough, erect, quadrilateral, branches few. Opposite leaves, lower ones connate, pinnatilobate with irregular crenate edges. Tiny flowers in filiform spikes forming a terminal panicle.
Habitat	Originally probably a Eurasian species, nowadays naturalized in North America. Grows on wasteland from lowland to foothill elevations.
Collection	The upper part of the flowering stem is collected and mixed with the young leaves.
Drying	Dry in thin layers in a current of air (artificial heat 35°-40°C; 95°-104°F).
Cultivation	Prefers heavy, damp soils, rich in nitrogen. Cultivation unnecessary — a weed.
Active constituents	The most important is the bitter glycoside iridoid verbenaline, then tannins, mucilages, saponins, silica and quinones.
Efficacy	Adstringens, diureticum, diaphoreticum, galactogogum, antineuralgicum.
Use	A plant long known to popular medicine, now again arousing great interest on account of its iridoid verbenaline content. Antineuralgic effect mainly in cases of migraine, also effective for anaemia and chlorosis.
Dosage	A 5 per cent infusion (leave to stand 15 minutes), 2-3 cups a day. As the active principles affect the muscles of the uterus the drug and preparations containing it should not be prescribed for pregnant women.

For external use, infusions of around 10 per cent are used for inflammations of the mouth cavity, for compresses (e.g. painful, swollen lymph glands), suppurating wounds, swellings, skin eruptions, haematomas.

The herb is also thought to be of help in dissolving kidney stones, for which the juice is recommended: 50g of the fresh herb is chopped finely or crushed in a mortar, squeezed through a cloth and mixed with equal quantities of wine vinegar; leave to stand 14 days in a warm place and then filter; 8 drops three times a day.

Warning	Related cultivated species are *not* collected.

COMMON SPEEDWELL, HEATH SPEEDWELL

15-30cm (6-12in) — ‡

(+) *Veronica officinalis*

Flowers: June-September

Scrophulariaceae

Caution

(+) *Herba Veronicae* — herbage

Botanical description	Creeping, decumbent stems; opposite, ovate, hairy leaves with finely dentate edges. Flowers on short pedicels forming terminal spikes.
Habitat	Abundant throughout Europe, from lowland to subalpine elevations on heaths, meadows, in deciduous, coniferous and mixed forests.
Collection	The aerial parts are cut off at the beginning of the flowering period and dried quickly in thin layers.
Cultivation	Likes both sandy and loamy soils, shallow, easily drying and acid on the surface. Dislikes limestone. Circumpolar species — abundant.
Active constituents	Mainly bitter substances, tannins, the iridoid aucubine, silica, saponin, organic acids and mineral salts.
Efficacy	Stomachicum, expectorans, depurativum — metabolicum, tonicum, antisepticum.
Use	An ancient medicinal plant, very universal. To this day known above all as a stomachic assisting digestion and as an expectorant. It helps with the excretion of harmful substances produced by the metabolic processes of the organism and has an antibacterial effect on the mucous membrane of the epidermis. It is still popular believed to have antipyretic and diaphoretic properties.
Dosage	The usual infusion: one teaspoonful of the drug to a glass of water, ½ glass 2-3 times a day before meals. The herbage drug is rarely used alone; it is usually combined with the herbage of Horse-tail, Common Knotgrass, Centaury as a depurative and tonic; as an expectorant with Cowslip flower and Garden Thyme herbage.. For external use a decoction is made of 1½ teaspoonfuls of the drug to 1½ glasses of water: cover and boil gently 5 minutes. Use as a gargle, for compresses or rinses.
Warning	Popular medicine overestimates the efficacy of Common Speedwell.

SWEET VIOLET

Viola odorata
Violaceae

10-15cm (4-6in) — ‡
Flowers: March-April
(again August-November)

Radix Violae — root; *Herba Violae* — herbage; *Flores Violae* — flower

Botanical description	Short rhizome, long stolons and basal rosette. Petioled, cordate leaves with short hairs. Fragrant, symmetrical flower with a spur.
Habitat	A fairly common European species in deciduous woods and scrub lowland to mountain elevations. There are many related North American species.
Collection	Practically the whole plant is used for therapeutic purposes. The flower is of greater value when collected from shady spots. The rhizomes together with the roots are pulled up in autumn and washed briefly.
Drying	The flowering herbage, rhizomes and roots are dried quickly spread out in a well-aired, shady place: artificial heat up to 50°C (122°F) for the herbage, rhizomes and roots up to 40°C (104°F). The flower is dried in the usual way.
Cultivation	Propagated by dividing the roots; also possible from seeds. Prefers soils rich in nutrients, nitrogen and humus.
Active constituents	The main active substances throughout the plant are saponins, then silica; the flowers contain blue colouring. The alkaloid violin is now believed to be without effect.
Efficacy	Expectorans, secretolyticum; flower also a nervinum.
Use and dosage	Official medicine sometimes uses the root as a secretolyticum (a decoction of 2g of the drug in 170ml of water). Used by the teaspoonful especially in cases of dry bronchitis *(bronchitis sicea)*. Extracts from the root also have an antimycotic effect. The leaf is used in popular medicine as a diaphoretic (3 teaspoonfuls for an infusion or maceration; the odoratin present in it lowers the blood pressure. The flower is the part most often collected. It is used fresh to make crystallised sweets and aromatic vinegar. Often used to make a cough syrup and alleviate insomnia in children and elderly people (an infusion of 50g of the flower to 100ml of water; leaves to stand 24 hours, add 150g sugar and heat for 20 minutes, don't boil, then strain).

A maceration can be made from the flowers (2 teaspoonfuls to 2 glasses of water), for use as an expectorant and nervine, for skin diseases, etc.

HEARTSEASE, WILD PANSY

Viola tricolor
Violaceae
Herba Viola tricoloris — herbage; *Flores Violae tricoloris* — flower

10-20cm (4-8in) — * — ‡
Flowers: May-October

Botanical description	Hollow, branching stem, erect or ascending. Leaves ovate or oblong lanceolate. Pinnate stipules. Single flowers usually of three colours on long petioles. A very variable plant with many sub-species and hybrids.
Habitat	A weed found in fields, by the wayside, in gardens, occasionally on mountain pastures throughout Eurasia.
Collection	Collect the flowering herbage without the roots. The flower is picked before it is in full bloom.
Drying	In well-ventilated layers not more than 1cm (½in) thick.
Cultivation	The seeds are sown out where required, among grass or clover, and the plant will then propagate itself.
Active constituents	Flavones (rutin), anthocyanins — pigments, carotenoids, saponins, silica containing fragrant violutoside (menthyl salicylate glucoside).
Efficacy	Diureticum, expectorans, tonicum, diaphoreticum, metabolicum.
Use	The drugs are reliable diuretics, also expectorants and metabolic agents; their beneficial effect in the treatment of eczema and other skin defects has been proved. They are an adjuvant for blood capilliary ruptures and help the skin to regenerate after irradiation by harmful X-rays.
Dosage	Usually an infusion, 2 teaspoonfuls of the drug to 2 glasses of water, sip throughout the day. The drug can also be macerated or boiled briefly for the extraction of further substances. The same dosage is recommended for external use. Only occasionally used by itself usually combined.
Warning	The dosage must not be increased unnecessarily or it will provoke vomiting (on account of the saponins). The large-flowered cultivated variety of pansy is of no therapeutic value.

MISTLETOE

(+) *Viscum album*
Loranthaeae
(+) *Herba Visci albi* — herbage

20-50cm (8-20cm) — ††
Flowers: March-April
Caution

Botanical description	Woody evergreen, semi-parasitic on the branches of trees. Round stems; coriaceous leaves, elongatedly ovate, obtuse. Inconspicuous flowers forming terminal heads in the leaf axils.
Habitat	Parasitic plant growing on both deciduous and coniferous trees throughout Europe. American mistletoe is a different plant, *Phoradendron flavescens*.
Collection	The young tops of the leafy branches can be collected the whole year round.
Drying	Dry by artificial heat (the only possible method in winter — maximum 40°C; 104°F).
Cultivation	Practically impossible. The seeds are scattered by birds.
Active constituents	Mainly peptides, which also represent the toxic principle of Mistletoe, viscotoxin (from which amino acids are obtained by hydrolysis). Others are choline, acetylcholine, triterpenoids, saponins, flavones, sugars, pigments and mucilage (sometimes called viscin).
Efficacy	Metabolicum, hypotensivum, antiarythmicum, antiscleroticum.
Use	Water and alcohol extracts from Mistletoe have a mainly metabolizing effect; they lower the blood pressure, are beneficial for arteriosclerosis and regulate the beating of the heart. They can be used as an adjuvant for bleeding and excessive menstrual flow. The drug inhibits malignant growths but as it is very toxic, its therapeutic use is limited. The therapeutic dose is very near to the toxic dose.
Dosage	The usual dosage for an infusion is ½-1 teaspoonful to 1-1½ glasses of water (macerate 10 minutes). Drink ¼-⅓ glass, 2-3 times a day. Mistletoe is often an ingredient in antisclerotic and cardiac herbal teas.
Warning	Do not confuse Mistletoe with the similar deciduous species, *Loranthus europaeus* or *Phoradendron flavescens*.

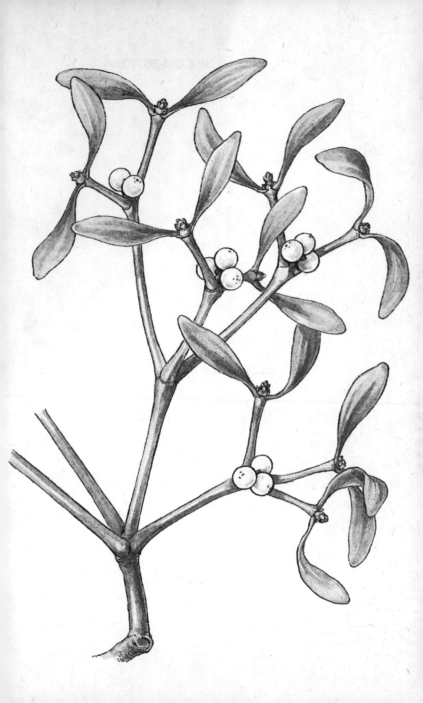

CALENDAR OF COLLECTION

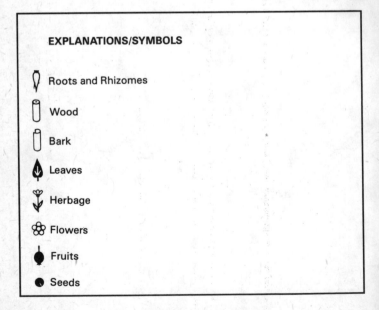

EXPLANATIONS/SYMBOLS

Roots and Rhizomes

Wood

Bark

Leaves

Herbage

Flowers

Fruits

Seeds

Name	Page	*Months* 1	2	3	4	5	6	7	8	9	10	11	12
Agrimony *Agrimonia eupatoria*	42						●	●	●				
Alpine Bearberry *Arctostaphylos uva-ursi*	50			●	●	●			●	●			
Angelica *Angelica archangelica*	48									●	●		
Arnica *Arnica montana*	52						●	●	●	●	●		
Autumn Crocus *Colchicum autumnale*	72						●	●					
Belladonna *Atropa belladonna*	56						●	●			●		
Bilberry *Vaccinium myrtilus*	198					●	●	●	●	●			
Blackberry *Rubus fruticosus*	166						●	●	●	●			
Blackcurrant *Ribes nigrum*	160						●	●	●				
Blackthorn *Prunus spinosa*	154			●	●	●				●	●		
Bogbean *Menyanthes trifoliata*	134						●	●					
Borage *Borago officinalis*	60					●	●	●	●				
Broad-leaved Lime *Tilia platyphyllos*	192						●	●					
Burnet Saxifrage *Pimpinella saxifraga*	144			●	●		●	●	●	●	●	●	
Centaury *Centaurium minus*	66							●	●	●	●		
Chamomile *Matricaria chamomilla*	126					●	●	●	●				

Name	Page	1	2	3	4	5	6	7	8	9	10	11	12
Chicory *Cichorium intybus*	70									●	●		
Club Moss *Lycopodium clavatum*	122						Spores						
Coltsfoot *Tussilago farfara*	194			●	●	●	●	●	●				
Comfrey *Symphytum officinale*	182					●	●	●	●	●	●	●	
Common Flax *Linum usitatissimum*	120									●	●		
Common Fumitory *Fumaria officinalis*	90					●	●	●	●	●			
Common Horse-tail *Equisetum arvense*	82				Spores	●	●	●	●				
Common Juniper *Juniperus communis*	112		●	●						●	●		
Common Knotgrass *Polygonum aviculare*	148						●	●	●	●			
Common Mallow *Malva sylvestris*	124					●	●	●	●	●			
Common Oak *Quercus robur*	158			●	●	●			●	●	●	●	
Common Sage *Salvia officinalis*	172					●	●	●	●	●			
Common Speedwell *Veronica officinalis*	206						●	●	●				
Common Toadflax *Linaria vulgaris*	118						●	●	●	●			
Coriander *Coriandrum sativum*	76							●	●				
Cowberry *Vaccinium vitis-idaea*	200						●	●	●	●	●		
Cowslip *Primula veris*	152			●	●					●	●		
Dandelion *Taraxacum officinale*	186		●	●	●	●	●	●	●	●	●	●	
Dog Rose *Rosa canina*	162									●	●		

216

Name	Page	1	2	3	4	5	6	7	8	9	10	11	12
Downy Hemp-nettle *Galeopsis segetum*	94							flower	flower				
Elder *Sambucus nigra*	174					flower	flower		fruit	fruit			
Fennel *Foeniculum vulgare*	86									fruit	fruit		
Foxglove *Digitalis purpurea*	80						leaf	leaf	leaf				
Garden Thyme *Thymus vulgaris*	190					flower	flower	flower	flower				
Goat's Rue *Galega officinalis*	92							flower	flower	seed	seed		
Golden Rod *Solidago virgaurea*	180							flower	flower	flower			
Greater Celandine *Chelidonium majus*	68					flower	flower	flower	flower				
Ground Ivy *Glechoma hederacea*	100			flower	flower	flower	flower	flower					
Hawthorn *Crataegus oxyacanthoides*	78					leaf/flower	leaf/flower			fruit	fruit		
Heartsease *Viola tricolor*	210					flower	flower	flower	flower	flower			
Herb Bennet *Geum urbanum*	98			root	root					root	root	root	
Hop *Humulus lupulus*	106								Strobiles Lupulin				
Horse Chestnut *Aesculus hippocastanum*	40			bud/leaf/flower	leaf/flower	leaf/flower	leaf/flower		fruit	fruit	fruit		
Hyssop *Hyssopus officinalis*	110							flower	flower	flower			
Lady's Mantle *Alchemilla vulgaris*	44					flower	flower	flower	flower	flower			
Lg. — Fl. Sticky Eyebright *Euphrasia rostkoviana*	84							flower	flower	flower	flower		
Lemon Balm *Melissa officinalis*	130						leaf	leaf	leaf	leaf			
Licorice *Glycyrrhiza glabra*	102			root							root		

Name	Page	Months											
		1	2	3	4	5	6	7	8	9	10	11	12
Lily-of-the-Valley *Convallaria majalis*	74					●	●						
Ling *Calluna vulgaris*	62						●	●	●	●			
Lungwort *Pulmonaria officinalis*	156			●	●	●							
Marsh Mallow *Althaea officinalis*	46						●	●	●	●	●	●	
Mistletoe *Viscum album*	212	●	●									●	●
Motherwort *Leonurus cardiaca*	116					●	●	●	●	●			
Opium Poppy *Papaver somniferum*	142					Opium		●	●	●			
Peppermint *Mentha × piperita*	132						●	●	●	●			
Raspberry *Rubus idaeus*	168					●	●	●	●				
Ribbed Melilot *Melilotus officinalis*	128						●	●	●				
Ribwort Plantain *Plantago lanceolata*	146					●	●	●	●				
Rosemary *Rosmarinus officinalis*	164					●	●	●	●	●			
Rue *Ruta graveolens*	170					●	●	●	●	●			
Rupture-wort *Herniaria glabra*	104						●	●	●	●			
St. John's Wort *Hypericum perforatum*	108						●	●	●	●			
Shepherd's Purse *Capsella bursa-pastoris*	64			●	●	●	●	●	●	●			
Silver Birch *Betula pendula*	58			●	●	●	●						
Silverweed *Potentilla anserina*	150						●	●	●	●	●	●	
Soapwort *Saponaria officinalis*	176			●	●			●	●	●		●	●

Name	Page	Months											
		1	2	3	4	5	6	7	8	9	10	11	12
Spring Restharrow *Ononis spinosa*	138			🌷	🌷		🌷	🌷	🌷	🌷	🌷	🌷	
Stinging Nettle *Urtica dioica*	196			🌷	🌷	🌷	🌷	🌷	🌷	🌷	🌷		
Summer Savory *Satureia hortensis*	178						🌷	🌷	🌷				
Sweet Basil *Ocimum basilicum*	136						🌷	🌷	🌷				
Sweet Violet *Viola odorata*	208			🌷	🌷						🌷	🌷	
Tansy *Tanacetum vulgare*	184							🌷	🌷	🌸			
Valerian *Valeriana officinalis*	202					🌷	🌷	🌷	🌷	🌷	🌷	🌷	
Vervain *Verbena officinalis*	204							🌷	🌷	🌷			
White Dead-nettle *Lamium album*	114					🌸	🌸	🌸	🌸	🌸	🌸		
Wild Marjoram *Origanum vulgare*	140						🌷	🌷	🌷	🌷			
Wild Strawberry *Fragaria vesca*	88					🍓	🍓	🍓					
Wild Thyme *Thymus serpyllum*	188				🌷	🌷	🌷	🌷	🌷				
Wormwood *Artemisia absinthium*	54						🌷	🌷	🌷	🌷			
Yarrow *Achillea millefolium*	38						🌷	🌷	🌷	🌷	🌷		
Yellow Gentian *Gentiana lutea*	96		🌷	🌷						🌷	🌷	🌷	

INDEX OF COMMON NAMES